Automotive
Air Conditioning

Automotive Air Conditioning

LESLIE F. GOINGS
*M. Ed., Instructor, Automotive Technology,
Henry Ford Community College, Dearborn,
Michigan. Member, American Vocational
Association.*

American Technical Society ⓐⓈ Chicago 60637

Preface

An automotive air conditioner is a system with few moving parts. Nothing moves but the gas, driven by the compressor. Inside the car the control switches select the cooling or heating modes desired. The system responds with the appropriate tempered air, pushed by blowers.

It is the objective of this text to present a basic approach to installation and service. Systematically the student learns in detail the correct and practical steps to follow in trouble shooting. He checks pressures, finds leaks, or locates inoperative parts.

Where laboratory work is emphasized, the basic trouble-shooting material of Chapter 4 may be presented along with the fundamentals given in the first three chapters.

A most detailed coverage of the compressor and its clutch are given in Chapter 5. Although these are specialty shop operations, every good air conditioning mechanic should know them.

A set of trouble-shooting procedures and tests, with detailed explanations, teaches the student the practical techniques and procedures for servicing almost any installation. The book is illustrated throughout with examples from the major automotive manufacturers. A *Glossary* of air conditioning terms is also appended for easy reference.

The Publishers.

Contents

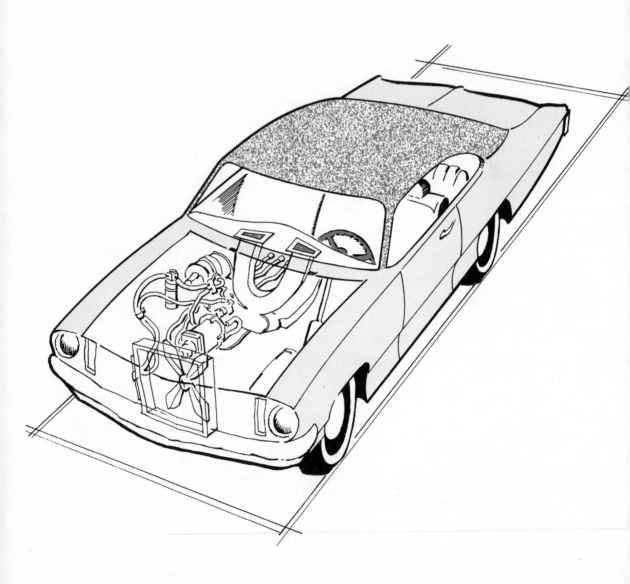

Principles of Auto Air Conditioning

1

Chapter 1 is a general introduction to the fundamental concepts of auto air conditioning. Human comfort and the factors that influence our comfort are discussed in this chapter. The scientific principles which are necessary to have an air conditioner operate to provide us with comfort are presented.

After thoroughly understanding the information in this chapter, you will be able to proceed readily to the actual servicing of the air conditioning system in your car.

Today, air conditioning (cooling and dehumidifying) on automobiles is an increasingly popular accessory. Figures show that almost 60 percent of the new cars are ordered with factory-installed, air-conditioning units. In the warmer southern climates, this figure approaches 90 percent or more.

In the past, an air-conditioned car was a luxury and the air conditioner added considerably to the retail value. This is still true, but to a lesser extent. In fact, the car that is not air conditioned is often more difficult to sell.

Why is air conditioning so much more popular now? The most logical reason is that the purchaser of the automobile is interested in more than just transportation. The new car buyer wants comfort while he is in his vehicle. Several years ago, jokes were made about the fellow working in his air-conditioned office, living in an air-conditioned home, shopping in air-conditioned stores and driving an air-conditioned car. Today these statements are not jokes, but real life situations. Farmers work their fields in large air-conditioned tractors. Many large highway trucks are equipped with air conditioning. Taxis and police cars are also air conditioned, even in northern areas. Any driver who is in his vehicle for the greater part of a working day would benefit from air conditioning.

With the large use of air-conditioning equipment, it is not at all unusual to find more and more automobiles with air conditioning as an accessory, either (1) factory installed or hung on by a service garage. All independently installed units are thus called (2) *hang-on* units.

It is interesting to note that air conditioning is beneficial to the vehicle owner or operator in ways other than just providing comfort. Safety is an important factor. On a hot day, a driver who has been operating an air-conditioned car or truck is much less fatigued than one who has been driving without air conditioning.

The noise level is reduced in an air-conditioned car because windows are kept closed, eliminating distracting noises. Additionally, the security of the occupants and contents of the vehicle is improved. With doors locked and windows closed, the air conditioned vehicle is safer, more secure, and reasonably quiet in addition to being comfortable.

It has been stated that engine horsepower is used to operate the air conditioner. This power will cause a slight decrease in gasoline mileage. Usually the loss is approximately one or two miles per gallon depending on operating conditions. The extra fuel consumption is usually not large enough to cause the driver to turn off the air conditioner and roll down the vehicle windows. Rather, the slight additional cost of fuel is made up by a much more comfortable and safe ride. Cost of operation is a factor to be considered, but the average motorist will not care that much when his comfort is involved.

The major purpose of an air-conditioning system in an automobile is to provide

OUTSIDE AND INSIDE TEMPERATURE 95°; HUMIDITY 80%

OUTSIDE TEMPERATURE 95°, HUMIDITY 80%; INSIDE TEMPERATURE 75°, HUMIDITY 50%

Fig. 1-1. Human comfort factors.

comfort for the passengers and driver. In complete air conditioning, this involves not just cooling but also, at times, raising the temperature, as conditions of excessive hot or cold produce human discomfort. See Fig. 1-1.

This is the basic task which the automotive air conditioning system is designed to accomplish. In this book we will examine not just air cooling but also air heating, resulting in a comfortable driver and passengers regardless of the *ambient* air temperature (surrounding or outside temperature).

Comfort

Human comfort is an interesting topic and if we understand what makes us comfortable and why, we should then begin to see what an air conditioning system must do to keep us comfortable.

The human body usually has a deep body temperature of 98.6°F. The temperature of the skin and external parts of the body is somewhat lower, about 80° to 85°F. It can be seen that there is a difference between the two temperatures of approximately 13°F. What happens to cause the temperature to drop? Where does the body get the 98.6°F which is considered normal internal temperature for most of us?

As the body operates chemically, it is burning much as a fire burns. The fuel for our body is the stored energy it contains in the form of fat. As the body burns up this fat, heat is produced. This body heat must be removed or the body becomes very uncomfortable. However, this heat, if removed too rapidly will make the body uncomfortable. To help control body comfort, the temperature of the air which comes in contact with the body must not be too hot or too cold. The air must be moving so as to provide for the removal or addition of heat as required for comfort. In addition, if the moving air is clean of pollen and dust, and has excessive moisture removed, the body will enjoy controlled or conditioned air circulation.

Heat

In discussing comfort and cooling, reference was made to heat. Heat is a form of energy which is measured with a thermometer. Cold merely refers to a low temperature or a small amount of heat. Cold is the absence of heat. Air-conditioning systems provide humans with comfort by controlling the amount of heat in the moving air while at the same time reducing humidity and filtering harmful dust and pollen from the air.

Let's examine how the body removes heat and some of the underlying laws of thermodynamics which are basic to the refrigeration process.

As the body produces heat, it is carried away by convection, conduction, radiation and evaporation. A major law of thermodynamics is that *heat will always move from a hotter place to one which is cooler.* As the body then produces heat, this heat is lost to the surrounding atmosphere as the air temperature is usually

3

less than 98.6°F. If the air outside the body is 90°F, less heat will be lost or transferred than when the outside air is 40°F. We have all noticed this. When the heat moves rapidly away from our body we get cold. If the heat moves very slowly, we feel hot. An air-conditioning system attempts to control heat loss from the body to keep us from feeling too hot or too cold. Rather, we would like to keep the body in a comfort zone. Most people feel comfortable when the air temperature is 72°F to 80°F and the relative humidity of that air is 40 percent to 50 percent.

Humidity

Relative humidity is a measure of the amount of moisture in the air compared to the amount of moisture the air could actually hold at that particular temperature. A relative humidity of 50 percent indicates the air contains one half the moisture it could hold at that temperature.

The molecules which make up a substance can move about at various speeds. At slow speeds, the substance is usually solid. As heat is added, the molecules increase their activity, and a change from solid to liquid may occur. As more heat is added, molecular activity increases even more and the liquid will again change its state from liquid to vapor.

Molecular motion also affects water vapor. A cool vapor will have less molecular activity than a hotter vapor. When air is cool, the molecules are closer together due to less activity. As the cooler air is heavy, it does not have a great deal of space for water vapor. When air is heated, the molecules spread out, due to increased activity. The warmer air is lighter and will have more space between molecules for water vapor. Therefore, warm air can hold much more water vapor than cool air.

Automotive, as well as household, air-conditioning systems must be able to lower the temperature of the air, dry out excess moisture, and filter out the dust and pollen while also providing for circulation of the air within the conditioned area.

Comfort is also affected by the humidity level. An air conditioner is able to partially control humidity. Moisture present in the air can be seen when the action of water evaporating or boiling from a heated pan is examined. As the pan of water absorbs heat, eventually the water will boil away. Soon all the water will disappear. When a liquid such as water is changed to a vapor, the vapor enters the surrounding air. The water has merely changed from a liquid to a gas. When this happens, several things have occurred. For the water to evaporate, it must have gained heat to cause the liquid to change to a vapor. This heat was received from an energy source and transferred to the water. The water vapor then enters and combines with the atmospheric air. Thus, for water to become a vapor, it must be heated enough to vaporize.

In the human body, perspiration is on our skin at most times. When the weather is hot and the body sweats or perspires, the water is not being readily vaporized from the skin into the air. This makes us feel uncomfortable. If the air has a high humidity level, it is not able to accept moisture from other sources, such as our body. High temperatures and high relative humidity result in our feeling uncomfortable. Cold air with less heat and less humidity will tend to remove moisture too rapidly from our body. This can make us feel very cold and often will lead to dry lips and cracked skin. For comfort, the body requires a certain amount of humidity; too much or too little produces discomfort. Humidity below 30 percent and above 60 percent are levels which are uncomfortable to the majority of persons.

Absolute humidity is a measure of the actual water vapor in a given volume of air, but absolute humidity does not impart any information on how much water could be held at a given temperature and pressure; thus the term *relative humidity* is used. Relative humidity is a comparison of the amount of moisture present in the air to the maximum amount of moisture the air can hold at that particular temperature. Vapor is measured as a grain of water per cubic foot of air. Examples of the effect of humidity would be, air at 32°F which could hold 2 grains of moisture, and air at 70°F which could hold 8 grains of moisture. In both cases we have 100 percent relative humidity.

If the air at 32°F were heated to 70°F, the 70°F air would then have a relative humidity of 25 percent, whereas if the same air were cooled to 32°F its relative humidity would be 100 percent. Note also that the total capacity for moisture is much greater with 70°F air as compared to 32°F air. (See *Psychrometric Chart* in Appendix for equations and calculations of relative humidity of air at various temperatures.)

Atmospheric pressure also influences the amount of humidity by allowing more moisture to vaporize at low pressures and less vapor to combine with air at higher pressures.

The effect of entering and leaving a swimming pool is a good example of how temperature and humidity affect comfort. When our body is in a pool, we feel cold or warm depending on the temperature difference between our body and the water. If the water is 50°F we will feel cold because our body gives up heat to the cooler water. If the temperature of the water is 75°F, the water will feel better because less heat is removed from the body by the warmer water.

The effect of humidity can be observed when stepping out of the water. If the humidity is low or it is windy, the rate of water evaporation from the wet body will be rapid. The individual then feels chilled due to the rapid loss of body heat used to evaporate the water and finally dry the skin. If the body is covered when leaving the water, the rate of evaporation is slowed down and the body will not feel as chilled. When the body is dry (excess moisture removed), it feels more comfortable because the rapid rate of evaporation will have slowed.

Moisture content of the air determines how much water vapor can be removed from the body. If the air is humid, it will contain nearly all of the water vapor it can hold. High relative humidity also causes slow vaporization of moisture. Many times, comfort can be greatly improved by merely controlling the amount of moisture in the air. (See comfort chart and Temperature-Humidity Index on which it was based in the Appendix.) A fan blowing across our face feels good when we are warm, even if the air is not cooled. It feels cooler because heat is removed from the face faster with the fan. Also the rate of moisture evaporation is increased. If a fan is directed at us in a

5

cold room, the same conditions exist again and moisture is vaporized more rapidly along with heat from the body.

Since the initial temperature is lower, the body now will feel cooler, and thus probably uncomfortable.

Vehicle Cooling

To cool a vehicle adequately is a very difficult job for an air-conditioning unit. The heat in the vehicle is removed by the cooling process, but as soon as a door is opened the warmer outside air will move into the cooler interior, and the air conditioner has to virtually start all over again. Homes and buildings have a storage effect which retains cool air for some time when the system is shut down. A vehicle has little capacity for retaining temperature when a door is opened or the air conditioner is turned off.

In addition to atmospheric heat, the heat load on the unit is increased by more passengers. Each warm body requires the unit to perform more work. Radiation from the sun through the large glass areas of the vehicle also adds to the heat load on the unit. The engine heat produced under the hood and the heat produced on the floor by the exhaust and the transmission also tends to flow up into the vehicle interior. These factors plus reflected heat from the pavement and the heat of other nearby vehicles all add to the total heat load.

Colors used in vehicle paint and upholstery also influence the heat load. Light colors and smooth surfaces reflect radiant heat better than dark, rough surfaces. Insulation added to the vehicle wherever possible, especially the roof, is also beneficial.

Most air-conditioned cars are sold with tinted glass to reduce the effect of radiant heat from the sun. The large glass areas found on the automobile allow a great deal of radiant heat to enter the vehicle. Tinted glass will reduce the heat load through the glass by approximately 40 percent. The degree of tint used, however, must be a compromise between adequate night visibility and radiant heat reduction. Glare is also reduced with tinted glass.

Automotive air-conditioning systems make use of several components and a special refrigerant to provide comfort within the vehicle. These components utilize conduction, convection and radiation to remove heat from the interior of the vehicle and transfer this removed heat to the outside of the vehicle. The car is cooled by removing or transferring heat from the inside to the outside of the vehicle. With circulation of cool, clean, dry air, it is possible to improve the comfort level of the interior of a vehicle considerably.

How this heat transfer is performed and why it is possible will be explained further.

Condensation

The manner in which an air conditioner controls humidity requires an understanding of the meaning of the term *dew point.* We have all observed dew outside in the mornings. Sometimes the dew is heavy and other times it is light. Dew is water that has condensed out of the air. When air is cooled it can hold less vapor. When the temperature of air reaches the dew point, water condenses out of the air into water droplets.

Since air-conditioning units also cool air, water will condense out of the air as the air temperature is lowered. This water removal by cooling is called *dehumidifying.* The water drains out to the road surface through drain tubes or openings provided in the air-conditioner unit.

As this water washes or rolls down the air conditioner, the condensed water tends to wash dirt off the moistened surfaces, and this provides a cleaning action by removing dust and pollen that is in the incoming air. It is in this manner that the automotive air conditioner is said to filter or clean the air. Normally, no special filter material is provided with an automobile air conditioner.

Air conditioners do not have any provision for changing the odor or fragrance of the air coming through the unit. Frequently, on first use, an air conditioner will deliver foul smelling air until it has become fully operative. This is particularly true if the occupants smoke frequently. Smoking tends to leave a residue which is not washed away readily by the condensing water.

Car owners are sometimes worried to see condensate water in a puddle on the driveway, or if the car is left on the lawn, it is common for the condensed water to stain or yellow the grass. This is due to an acidic action. The condensate is usually slightly acid rather than alkaline, thus causing yellowing of vegetation.

Heat Transfer

Conduction, convection and radiation are three basic methods used to transfer heat. Remember, when heat flows it is always from hot to warm, warm to cool or cool to cold.

Conduction is the movement of heat through an object or material. If a steel rod is heated at one end, eventually the opposite end of the rod will become warmer. The heat applied at one end travels through the steel rod to the cooler, unheated end. Heat is conducted by the rod. See Fig. 1-2.

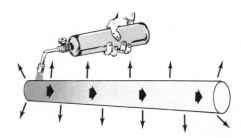

Fig. 1-2. Conduction by heat transfer through a solid substance.

Convection is the movement of heat through the air. Warm air is lighter than cold air. The air at the floor level is always cooler than air at ceiling height. Warm air moves upward and as it does it will be replaced by cooler, heavier air. Air circulation for air conditioning requires large air passages and strong blowers to force colder air into the higher heated areas of a room or vehicle to overcome convection. See Fig. 1-3.

Radiation is a form of heat transfer which uses heat rays and is independent of air temperatures. On a cold day, we often can feel the warmth radiated by the sun through the cold air. Sitting

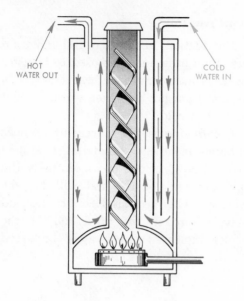

Fig. 1-3. Convection is heat transfer by currents: heated air will rise; hot water will also rise.

near a cold window, we might feel cold. Body heat is radiating to the cool window. Rapid loss of body heat makes the body feel cool. Fig. 1-4.

Convection, conduction and radiation are being utilized constantly in combination to provide the proper level of comfort in air-conditioning systems.

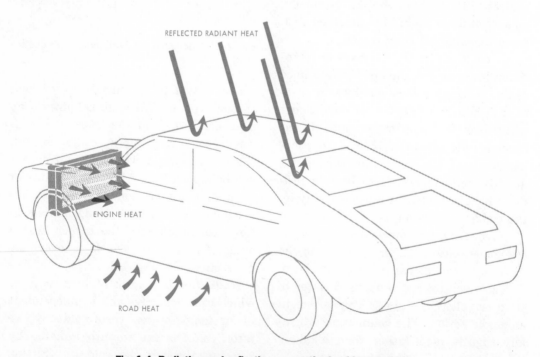

Fig. 1-4. Radiation and reflection are methods of heat transfer.

Principles of Refrigeration

To understand how the air conditioner can perform its task it is helpful to examine how a quantity of water, which is a common substance, reacts to heat differences. As water is heated and cooled, or rather as heat is added or removed from water, certain changes take place.

Water is a liquid, ice is solid water, and steam is water vapor or gas. The difference between these three states of water lies in the amount of heat the water contains.

A BTU (*British Thermal Unit*) is the common method of measuring the amount of heat in a substance. One BTU is the amount of heat needed to raise the temperature of one pound of water one degree Fahrenheit at sea level or standard atmospheric pressure.

One BTU is also equal to 252 calories, or 778 pound feet of mechanical energy. The BTU referred to in air conditioning is a *measure of heat quantity*.

Refer to Fig. 1-5, which charts the caloric (or heat) absorption of water as it goes from solid to liquid, to gas. Notice

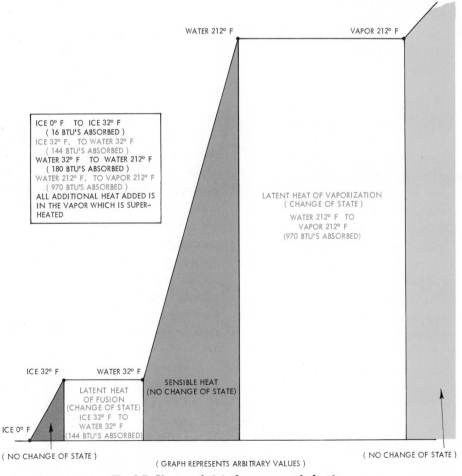

ICE 0° F TO ICE 32° F
(16 BTU'S ABSORBED)
ICE 32° F. TO WATER 32° F
(144 BTU'S ABSORBED)
WATER 32° F TO WATER 212° F
(180 BTU'S ABSORBED)
WATER 212° F. TO VAPOR 212° F
(970 BTU'S ABSORBED)
ALL ADDITIONAL HEAT ADDED IS
IN THE VAPOR WHICH IS SUPER-
HEATED

WATER 212° F

VAPOR 212° F

LATENT HEAT OF VAPORIZATION
(CHANGE OF STATE)

WATER 212° F TO
VAPOR 212° F
(970 BTU'S ABSORBED)

ICE 32° F

WATER 32° F

SENSIBLE HEAT
(NO CHANGE OF STATE)

LATENT HEAT
OF FUSION
(CHANGE OF STATE)
ICE 32° F TO
WATER 32° F
(144 BTU'S ABSORBED)

ICE 0° F

(NO CHANGE OF STATE)

(NO CHANGE OF STATE)

(GRAPH REPRESENTS ARBITRARY VALUES)

Fig. 1-5. Change of state for one pound of water.

that one pound of water at 32°F will not necessarily be ice. Experiments have shown that 144 BTU's must be removed from water at 32°F to cause it to change to ice at 32°F. Obviously heat (BTU's) was removed, but no temperature change was noted!

The heat necessary to cause a *change of state* but with no temperature change is known as *latent heat*. Latent means *hidden* heat. As the liquid changes to a solid, the process is called *fusion*. Therefore, the *latent heat of fusion* for one pound of water is 144 BTU's. Note that with water frozen, however, each single BTU removed now causes a temperature change of 2 degrees F down to zero Fahrenheit.

As a liquid at 32°F, the temperature of one pound of water will increase one degree F for each BTU, up to 212°F. In these two cases, the removal or the addition of a BTU causes a noticeable temperature change. This change can be seen on a thermometer and as the water temperature is increased from 32°F to 212°F our senses would tell us the temperature had increased. If we placed a finger in the water at 32°F and 100°F the temperature change would be obvious. This increase in temperature is called *sensible heat*. Sensible heat is measurable. Latent heat is not easily measured. No change of state takes place with sensible heat.

Note again that the water is now at 212°F but it still does not boil or change state. A considerable amount of heat, actually 970 BTU's, needs to be added before the liquid water at 212°F will boil and become vapor at 212°F. The 970 BTU's are latent or hidden heat. Since the liquid is vaporizing, the term *latent*

TABLE 1-1. LATENT HEAT OF VAPORIZATION VALUES	
LIQUID	BTU PER POUND
WATER	970
AMMONIA	565
ALCOHOL	367
SULFUR DIOXIDE	170
METHYL CHLORIDE	178
FREON 12	70

heat of vaporization is used. See Table 1-1.

As the vapor picks up more BTU's, its temperature also increases, and it is now a *super-heated vapor*. The water that remains will continue to boil at 212°F.

It should be pointed out that the reverse action of changing steam at 212°F to water at 212°F would require the *removal* of 970 BTU's per pound.

Pressure

Another factor which influences the thermal action of water or any liquid which is to be changed to a vapor is pressure. The air which we breathe exerts a pressure all about us. We tend to forget atmospheric pressure, which is 14.7 pounds per square inch (psi) at sea level. As we go above sea level, less air would be pushing on us. Lower elevations have a higher atmospheric pressure. This pressure has a direct effect on the vaporization or boiling point of liquids. See Fig. 1-6.

A common example of the effect of pressure on the boiling points of water is found in the automobile cooling system. All present radiators use pressure caps. When the water in a radiator is under pressure it can absorb more heat from the engine and yet the water will not

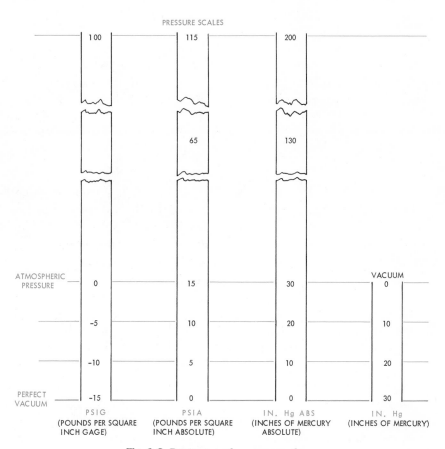

Fig. 1-6. Pressure and vacuum scales.

boil. The temperature of the water can go as high as 250°F with a 13-pound pressure cap and the water will not boil. This increased pressure allows the liquid to absorb more heat and also prevents the molecules from moving so rapidly as to become vaporized. When the pressure is removed the molecules can move more freely and the water will vaporize. A one pound pressure increase will raise the boiling point of water 3¼°F.

Pressure and Vapors

Pressure above atmospheric pressure can be used to cause a vapor to return to a liquid state. Pressure which is less than atmospheric pressure is called a *vacuum*. A vacuum, as the term is commonly used, is a *low pressure*, namely less than 14.7 psi. A liquid will vaporize faster if it is subjected to vacuum. The greater the vacuum the lower the boiling point.

So far, it has been determined that pressure can affect boiling points. The stated boiling point of most liquids is the sea level pressure boiling point, but any change in pressure causes a change in the boiling point, as also shown in Fig. 1-6.

The air pressure the weatherman reports is recorded on a device called a *barometer*. Day to day variations in the barometric readings help to predict weather changes. Understanding the examples and principles of how water reacts to heat and pressure are necessary if one is to understand refrigeration. In air conditioning service, various pressures within the system are used for specific reasons. Also the materials used for service are under pressure, or utilize vacuum.

Refrigerants

Water is a good example to use for explanatory reasons. However, water is not a practical refrigerant. The reason for the impracticality of water as a refrigerant is that its boiling point is too high. In air conditioning units, materials called *refrigerants* are used which boil at much lower temperatures. Boiling requires the addition of heat regardless of a substance's temperature or boiling point.

Refrigerant-12 (R-12), the most common refrigerant in automotive use,[1] has a boiling point of −21.7°F. Compared with water's boiling point of 212°F, this seems a very low boiling point, but remember that for a substance to change from liquid to vapor, *latent heat of vaporization* is utilized, whatever the temperature. Whether water or R-12 is used, a certain number of BTU's are required to produce boiling. The boiling point is dependent on the material itself. Since the latent heat of vaporization of R-12 is approximately 70 BTU's per pound at 5°F, Table 1-2, this means that R-12 will boil with a very small amount of heat.

Water with its boiling point of 212°F, or alcohol which boils at 160°F, would not be good refrigerants in the range of 70 to 100°F. A substance which boils below 70 to 80°F is needed to bring about the desired comfort. R-12, which boils at −21.7°F is nearly ideal as a refrigerant. It can operate at fairly low pressures and will condense in a temperature range over which most vehicles operate.

R-12 is commonly called *Freon*, which is the trade name of I.E. DuPont de Nemours and Co. The chemical formula is

TABLE 1-2. TEMPERATURE-PRESSURE RELATIONSHIP OF R-12

FAHRENHEIT	PSI
−20	0.6
−15	2.4
−10	4.5
−5	6.7
0	9.2
5	11.8
10	14.6
15	17.7
20	21.0
25	24.6
30	28.5
35	32.6
40	37.0
45	41.7
50	46.7
55	52.0
60	57.7
65	63.8
70	70.2
75	77.0
80	84.2
85	91.8
90	99.8
95	108.3
100	117.2
105	126.6
110	136.4
115	146.8
120	157.7
125	169.1
130	181.0
135	193.5
140	206.6
145	220.3
150	234.6

1. See Group I Refrigerants in Appendix for other refrigerants.

Notice that the temperature-pressure relationships indicated by the color area are very close

C Cl$_2$ F$_2$. The chemical name is *dichloro-difluoromethane*. It is a derivative of carbon tetrachloride (C Cl$_4$) which was for-

merly a common cleaning fluid. Note that two fluorine atoms are added and two chlorine atoms removed to make R-12.

Safety Precautions in Handling Refrigerants

At room temperature (under pressure), R-12 is an odorless, colorless, tasteless, non-corrosive, non-flammable and low toxicity substance. With all these advantages R-12 is in most respects a safe refrigerant. But since it is under pressure and since it has such a low boiling point (−22°F), it requires special care when it is handled. Contact can "burn" your skin. (When liquid refrigerants evaporate they remove heat fast enough to cause body burns.)

Refrigerants Can Freeze Your Body

CAUTION:

Liquid R-12 should not ever be allowed to contact the skin or any part of the body. Severe frostbite can occur if even a drop is spilled on the skin. If the skin is accidentally exposed to R-12, treat for frostbite, which is a form of burn.

Refrigerants Can Damage Your Eyes

Great caution needs to be taken to prevent liquid refrigerant from coming in contact with eyes. To prevent eye damage, it is necessary to wear safety goggles.

CAUTION:

ALWAYS WEAR GOGGLES when servicing an air-conditioning system, or when handling LIQUID R-12!

If liquid R-12 should accidentally get into your eyes, rinse with a mineral oil immediately to absorb the liquid refrigerant. Follow with rinses of eye-wash or weak boric acid solution. Call a physician immediately for additional eye treatment.

Burning Refrigerant Makes a Deadly Gas

CAUTION:

In addition to the danger from refrigerant in the liquid state, there is another precaution. This stems from possible decomposition of refrigerant vapors when raised to high temperatures as in contact with an open flame. If decomposition results, the chief products are halogen acids which are corrosive and toxic. However, these acids are easly detected even in small concentrations by the human nose, serving as ample warning that decomposition has occurred. Also produced as a minor product in decomposition is phosgene which is also highly toxic.

Refrigerant Gas, Under Pressure, May Explode Container With Sufficient Heat

Since R-12 increases in pressure with an increase in heat, it is wise to avoid overheating the system or the refrigerant containers. For instance, if an air-conditioned vehicle is going to be placed in a paint bake oven, or if welding or steam cleaning is going to be performed near the refrigeration components, it is good practice to discharge or empty the refrigerant to prevent damage due to excessive pressures.

Often when adding R-12 (charging) the system, it is helpful to speed up the charging by placing the refrigerant in some warm water.

CAUTION:

Never use a flame or torch to speed up charging because an excessively fast pressure rise will occur and an explosion of the refrigerant container may occur.

Adequate ventilation is important, because a lack of oxygen may result if the air is heavily saturated with refrigerant vapor. Also the vapors, which are heavy, will stay in the area of the vehicle and could indicate, during testing, that there were leaks throughout the system.

CAUTION:

Always work with adequate ventilation.

SAFETY RULES SUMMARIZED:

To summarize briefly, when working with R-12:

1. DON'T TOUCH LIQUID R-12
2. WEAR SAFETY GOGGLES
3. AVOID EXCESSIVE HEAT
4. PROVIDE VENTILATION
5. AVOID FLAME

It is very important to protect the eyes and skin from contact with liquid R-12. The liquid can freeze the eye or skin on contact. Liquid R-12 is dangerous and proper eye protection is necessary to safely service air-conditioned cars. Safety goggles should be worn when servicing the system. The vapors of R-12 in an adequately ventilated area are not harmful.

Refrigeration

Once it is understood that a liquid *can absorb heat by boiling at a very low temperature*, the refrigeration process becomes easy to follow. Remember, the heat inside the vehicle is absorbed by a refrigerant, removed by the air conditioning system and discharged to the outside air.

How this actually takes place involves more scientific explanations.

Pressurization

Pressure on a liquid affects its boiling point. All present automotive liquid-cooling systems use pressure radiator caps.

This pressure cap increases the boiling point of the liquid coolant. Since it is not likely that the air temperatures would be as low as $-22°F$, except in rare instances, R-12 would be a vapor at ordinary temperatures. However, if this R-12 were placed under pressure so that boiling could not occur freely, it could be stored as a liquid and released when needed.

For complete vaporization to occur, the vapors must leave the surface of the liquid. If the container of liquid R-12 is *closed*, the liquid will boil and develop a pressure which will cause some vapor to condense and fall back into the liquid. So long as the container is closed, little heat is absorbed and the vapor is said to be *saturated*. A saturated vapor is one which is in contact with the liquid. As more heat is added the pressure will increase. If too much pressure develops, the container will explode.

Temperature-Pressure Relation

It is interesting to note that the temperature and pressure relationship of R-12 remains very much the same from 20°F to 75°F. This linear pressure-temperature relationship is useful in air conditioning service where checking various temperatures and pressures is necessary.

Note on the pressure-temperature chart, Table 1-2, that when the pressure of R-12 is 30 psi, the temperature is 28.5°F. It is helpful to the service man to remember that the pressure and temperature of R-12 are very much the same, particularly between 20°F and 75°F.

It is possible for temperatures to be measured with a scale other than the standard Fahrenheit. A Centigrade scale can also be used. Fig. 1-7 shows the relationship of these two different scales. Automotive service work will not require the use of a Centigrade thermometer, but mention is made of it because occasionally a Centigrade thermometer might be used and obviously the temperature readings would not correspond to the Fahrenheit scale. A conversion formula and chart is included in the *Appendix*.

Refrigeration Process Utilizes Temperature-Pressure Relationship

Why is the pressure relationship important? Let's look at a refrigeration cycle to see further what happens. In this simple diagram, Fig. 1-8, start with the liquid refrigerant at the expansion valve. Since R-12 is a liquid when it reaches the expansion valve it must be under fairly high pressure. As the expansion valve operates, it allows the liquid to enter the evaporator where the pressure is much lower. The liquid R-12 now is able to boil rapidly, thus absorbing heat from the air passing over the fins of the evaporator or cooling unit. Note that the liquid in the evaporator is not really evaporating as the name suggests, but it is vaporizing rapidly as the refrigerant absorbs heat. By the time the outlet pipe or tail pipe of the evaporator is reached, all of the liquid should be fully vaporized. Leaving the evaporator at this time is a cool vapor which will still absorb more heat. The vapor is now superheated as it has left the liquid. As this vapor superheats, it is directed to and drawn into the compressor. The area between the evaporator and compressor is called the *low side*. See Fig. 1-9.

The compressor draws in the vapors and compresses them into a small space. This high compression does two things to the once-cool vapor. It causes a pressure *increase*, which also causes a tem-

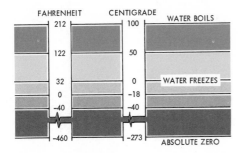

Fig. 1-7. Relationship of Fahrenheit and Centigrade scales.

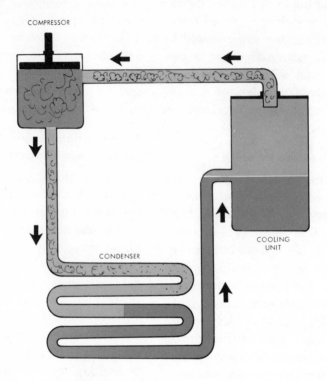

Fig. 1-8. Simple refrigeration cycle.

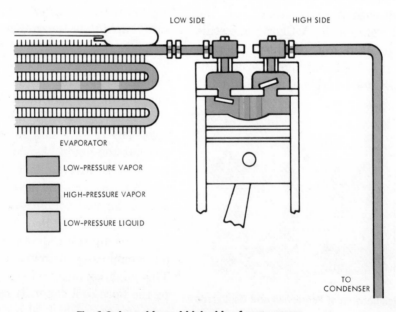

Fig. 1-9. Low side and high side of compressor.

perature *increase.* Therefore, the vapors leaving the compressor are *high-pressure, high-temperature vapors.* From the compressor to the evaporator is the *high-pressure side.*

The compressed hot vapors are delivered to the condenser, which is normally placed in front of the vehicle radiator. Air flows across the condenser as the vehicle is being operated. *Ram air* through the grill, and air pulled in by the fan, move across the surface of the condenser. (Ram air is forced across the front of the vehicle due to its forward motion.)

Since the hot vapors are now cooled by the outside air flowing across the condenser, the hot vapors will condense back to their liquid form. Remember that the temperature of the compressed gases might be 150°F or more on a hot day. The air flowing across the condenser might be 95°F. This puts the thermodynamic principle into operation. The gases in the condenser, being hot, will give up BTU's to the cooler air flowing past the outside of the condenser. This heat loss drops the temperature of the vapor enough so that it changes back into a liquid.

The liquid is hot and still under high pressure when it reaches the expansion valve again. This cycle repeats itself over and over. As long as no leaks occur, there is no loss of refrigerant and the cycle continues as long as the compressor is running.

What has happened is that the liquid R-12 has picked up BTU's from inside the vehicle and transferred this absorbed heat to the outside of the vehicle.

Receiver or Receiver-Drier

A receiver-drier (also called dehydrator) is used as a storage point for reserve liquid refrigerant. It also contains a material called a desiccant which picks up a very small amount of moisture that might be in the system. It is essential that moisture be removed. Moisture mixes with R-12 and causes a very corrosive acid to form which will eventually attack all metal components. Leaks and finally failure of the complete system will result if moisture is allowed to remain in the system. The effect of moisture and how it is removed will be discussed in Chapter 4.

Refrigeration Summary

The refrigeration cycle is: (1) Low-pressure liquid is in the evaporator. (2) Low-pressure vapor goes out and into the compressor where the vapors are compressed and sent to the condenser. (3) Cooler air across the condenser removes heat from the vapors causing condensation back into a liquid. (4) This hot, high-pressure liquid is passed into the receiver-drier and then back to the expansion valve which is located at the evaporator inlet. See Fig. 1-10.

Rating Air Conditioning Systems

The most common method of rating an air conditioner is in *BTU's per hour.* This is the accepted method of rating small units. In the past, air conditioners

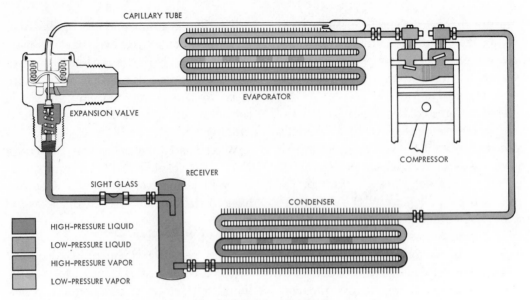

Fig. 1-10. Refrigeration cycle.

were rated by fractions of a ton. Larger air conditioners were rated by tons. If a ton of air cooling energy is understood, it is quite simple to see the relationship between BTU's/hour and a ton of cooling.

It is known that 144 BTU's will change one pound of ice at 32°F to water at 32°F. Then, if a ton equals 2000 pounds of ice, it would require 2000 times 144 or 288,000 BTU's to change a ton of ice to a ton of water at 32°F. For this amount of cooling to take place, a 24 hour time span is used. So it is then easy to compute that 288,000 BTU's divided by 24 hours will equal 12,000 BTU's/hr. Thus 288,000 BTU's in a 24-hour span, or 12,000 BTU's/hr, would equal *one ton of air cooling energy*.

Automotive air conditioning units are not normally rated by auto manufacturers with a BTU/hr rating. However, many independent makers are providing BTU ratings for their units. These range from 12,000 to 16,000 BTU/hr.

Several factors enter into an automotive air conditioner rating. Compressor size and speed are important. A large compressor operating at higher speeds can provide more refrigerant movement than a small, slow-running unit. The sizes of the condenser and the evaporator are also influencing factors. More refrigerant can be handled by a larger evaporator and so improved cooling is possible. This is also true with the condenser, for a large condenser will also expand system capacity.

Another factor is the expansion-valve flow rate. Many expansion valves will be rated in tons of cooling capacity. A typical automotive expansion valve is rated at 1¾ tons. That would equal 21,000 BTU's/hr.

Because these factors are so interrelated, expansion valve size, compressor size, evaporator and condenser size are engineered and designed to provide the best cooling arrangement possible within space limitations imposed by vehicle design and manufacture.

For these reasons, automotive units are not easily compared in terms of BTU ratings or component size.

Problems to Consider

1. Check several vehicles to determine how many are air conditioned. Also how many were factory equipped.
2. Demonstrate, using your own methods: *convection, conduction,* and *radiation.*
3. Check radiant heat by using two thermometers, one placed in front of a sheet of dark material, the other placed in front of a lighter material. A light bulb could be your heat source. Record and report your conclusions. Try several types of materials.
4. Record the temperature in a room at four different heights. What are your results, and why?
5. Using one pound or a fraction thereof of water, verify that additional heat is required to cause boiling after 212°F has been reached.
6. With a bell jar and vacuum pump reduce the pressure on a container of water with a thermometer in it. Observe and report your results.
7. Have your instructor place a small quantity of liquid R-12 in a glass. Be careful not to spill the liquid. Report your observations. Any odors?
8. With a thermometer taped to a refrigerant can, attach a pressure gage and note what the temperature pressure relationship is. Cool the can in cold water and then heat slightly with your hands. What happens? Exercise care when handling R-12 cans. USE SAFETY GOGGLES.

Trade Competency Check

1. What are two advantages in using air conditioning in an automobile? Name two disadtages.
2. What is the basic task of the air-conditioning system?
3. Define the word *cold.*
4. In what way can heat be removed or transferred?
5. What is a basic fact about heat movement?
6. What temperature and humidity range is usually most comfortable to humans?
7. What is meant by *relative humidity?*
8. What is dew? What is *dew point?*
9. How do air conditioners in automobiles clean the air which is discharged into the vehicle?
10. Explain what is meant by *conduction?*
11. Explain what is meant by *convection?*
12. Explain what *radiation* is.
13. What are the common states of matter?
14. What is a British Thermal Unit (BTU)?
15. What is *latent heat?*
16. What is *sensible heat?*
17. How do changes in pressure affect boiling points?
18. Why is liquid R-12 potentially dangerous?
19. What is the boiling point of Refrigerant-12?
20. What danger is present when working with R-12 vapors?
21. Why is R-12 considered a nearly ideal refrigerant?
22. What happens to the interior heat of an air-conditioned vehicle?
23. If the pressure in a container of R-12 is 70 psi, what do you know about the temperature of the refrigerant?
24. Explain the refrigeration cycle starting at the expansion valve.
25. What is a *ton* of air conditioning?

2

Components for Air Conditioners

Chapter 1 explained the purpose of air conditioning. Scientific principles were also discussed. In this chapter the operation of the automotive air conditioner is presented. The components which are used in the refrigeration process and also the controls, electric or vacuum type, will be explained. Together the mechanical cooling process and the manner and method of air distribution will be discussed. The understanding gained from this chapter in conjunction with the information in Chapter 1 will then provide a firm foundation on which testing service can be based.

Air Conditioner Components

The basic automotive air-conditioning system uses a compressor, an evaporator, a condenser, a receiver-drier and an expansion valve to provide for the removal and transfer of heat. See Fig. 2-1. This is true whether the system is of the factory-installed integral type or a hang-on type.

In addition to these basic components, other devices are used which provide control of the system, reduce noise, and protect the system from damage. See Fig. 2-2.

Electrical switches, resistors and relays are utilized to provide the system components with proper electrical energy when required.

Vacuum switches and motors (vacuum servos) are utilized to control the air flow from outside the vehicle into and out of the unit.

Thus, in addition to the mechanical refrigeration components, special electrical and vacuum devices need to be understood to adequately service auto air-conditioner complaints.

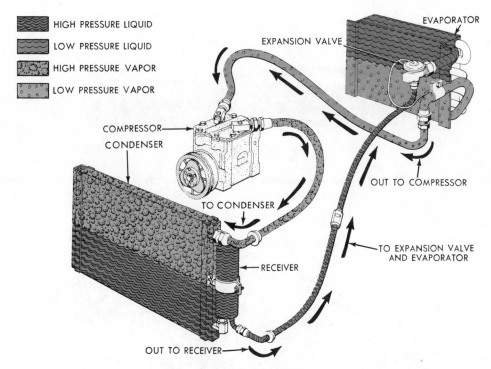

HIGH PRESSURE LIQUID
LOW PRESSURE LIQUID
HIGH PRESSURE VAPOR
LOW PRESSURE VAPOR

EVAPORATOR

EXPANSION VALVE

COMPRESSOR
CONDENSER

OUT TO COMPRESSOR

TO CONDENSER

TO EXPANSION VALVE
AND EVAPORATOR

RECEIVER

OUT TO RECEIVER

Fig. 2-1. Typical air-conditioning system.

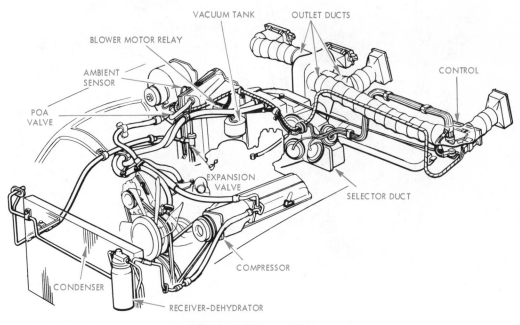

VACUUM TANK

OUTLET DUCTS

BLOWER MOTOR RELAY

AMBIENT
SENSOR

CONTROL

POA
VALVE

EXPANSION
VALVE

SELECTOR DUCT

COMPRESSOR

CONDENSER

RECEIVER-DEHYDRATOR

Fig. 2-2. Refrigeration system.

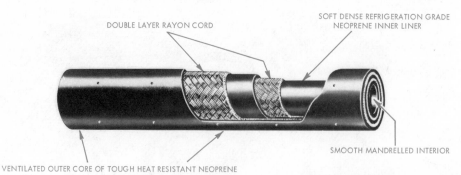

DOUBLE LAYER RAYON CORD

SOFT DENSE REFRIGERATION GRADE
NEOPRENE INNER LINER

SMOOTH MANDRELLED INTERIOR

VENTILATED OUTER CORE OF TOUGH HEAT RESISTANT NEOPRENE

Fig. 2-3. Refrigerant hose is specially designed to operate under high pressures and temperatures.

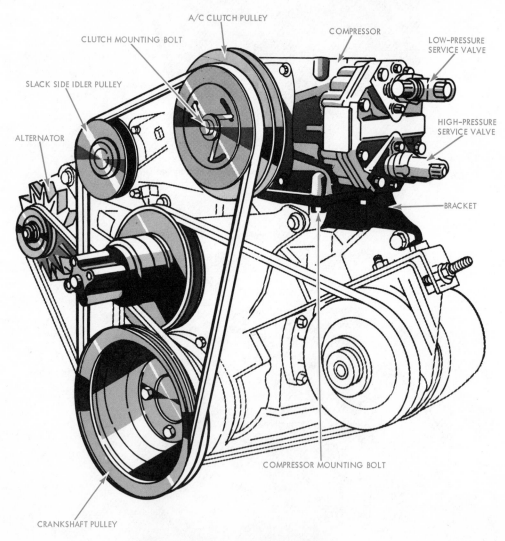

A/C CLUTCH PULLEY

CLUTCH MOUNTING BOLT

COMPRESSOR

LOW-PRESSURE
SERVICE VALVE

SLACK SIDE IDLER PULLEY

HIGH-PRESSURE
SERVICE VALVE

ALTERNATOR

BRACKET

COMPRESSOR MOUNTING BOLT

CRANKSHAFT PULLEY

Fig. 2-4. Typical compressor installation.

The evaporator is located in the cowl or under the dash on most vehicles. The condenser is usually placed in front of the cooling system radiator. The compressor is belt-driven and mounted on the engine. Connecting these major units are steel lines or special refrigerant hoses made of nylon or neoprene and fabric. See Fig. 2-3.

The refrigerant used in automotive units is called R-12 or Refrigerant-12. (Freon is a common trade name for R-12.) *Dichlorodifluoromethane* (CCl_2F_2) is the chemical name.)

Compressor

The typical air-conditioning compressor is mounted on the engine and driven by a belt, as shown in Fig. 2-4. The compressor can be started and stopped (by means of an electric clutch) any time the engine is running.

The compressor is used to create a suction or low pressure on the inlet side to pull vapors from the evaporator. These vapors are then compressed and discharged into the condenser. To do this, automotive air-conditioning compressors use one of three basic types of design. In-line two-cylinder and V-type two-cylinder compressors are frequently used and are very similar. Both use a crankshaft, connecting rods and two pistons, which are similar in operation to the same components in the internal combustion engine. See Figs. 2-5 and 2-6. These parts operate within a cylinder block which is enclosed with a valve plate and cylinder head.

A third type, called a six-cylinder compressor, uses three common cylinders and six pistons. In this design the pistons are arranged so as to move back and forth in the same plane as the compressor shaft. See Fig. 2-7.

Reed valves are used in these compressors. See Figs. 2-8 and 2-9. The valves enable gases to flow in one direction,

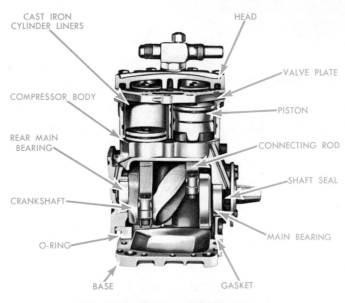

Fig. 2-5. Typical compressor section.

Fig. 2-6. Typical V-type compressor.

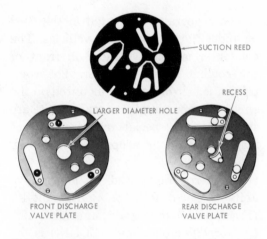

Fig. 2-8. Typical reed-type valves for six-cylinder G.M. compressor.

Fig. 2-7. Typical six-cylinder compressor.

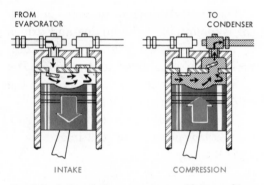

Fig. 2-9. Action in the compressor. Note reed-type valves.

either allowing gases to enter (suction) or to leave (discharge).

Compressors are rated in cubic inches of displacement. A compressor may range from 6 to 12 cubic inches in size. A large air conditioner requires the larger compressor. A small car would be able to use a smaller size compressor with no loss in efficiency. A larger compressor requires more engine power for its operation. Compressors work harder at higher speeds and are most efficient at high RPMs. Compressors of the two-cylinder type are made of either aluminum or cast iron. Aluminum is more popular because it is lighter in weight than the cast iron unit.

The compressor is usually equipped with valves to which test gages can be attached. However, service valves are also located at other points in some systems. With a little practice it becomes very easy to locate the service valves on different units. See Fig. 2-10, top and bottom for example.

TEFLON SEALS

SERVICE
VALVES

Fig. 2-10. Installed compressor with service valve; compressor with service valves removed.

The compressor is the one major component in the air-conditioning system that may fail because it has many more moving parts than any other component.

However, when failure occurs an exchange unit, new or rebuilt, is usually the most efficient way to get the system back into operation.

Aside from replacing a leaking compressor shaft seal, there is normally no major service to be performed. Compressor overhaul and rebuilding is generally done by the specialty shop or factory. The need for extremely clean and very dry conditions rule out service in the average shop. (Chapter 5 will discuss compressor service in greater detail.)

The compressor contains a supply of oil for lubrication. This special refrigeration oil mixes with the R-12 and is being circulated constantly throughout the complete system. There is normally no reason to be concerned about oil level in the compressor.

The only time oil level needs to be checked is when replacing a compressor or when a severe refrigerant leak causes a loss of oil. When a leak is located, this is quite obvious because of the oil residue at the leak area.

The six-cylinder compressor used by G.M. has no provision for checking oil level. Oil must be drained and measured with the compressor on the bench. Other compressors make provisions for use of a dipstick made of flat stock according to individual compressor specifications.

Oil in the air-conditioning system is not burned or otherwise consumed. It is in a sealed system and unless a large leak allows refrigerant and oil to escape, there is no reason to be concerned with oil level.

In the service section of this book, Chapter 5, more information can be found on adding oil.

Evaporator

The evaporator is the cooling unit. See Fig. 2-11. It consists of aluminum fins brazed to aluminum tubes. Aluminum or copper is used because of the high heat conductivity. Refrigerant flows through the tubes from the inlet to the outlet. The evaporator is housed in a casing which allows air from a blower to be forced across its surfaces. As this air flows across the evaporator, it will lose heat to the vaporizing R-12 inside. See Fig. 2-12 and 2-13. This air is then discharged into the vehicle directly or through a set of air flow tubes and ducts. The evaporator also contains provisions at the bottom of the case to allow moisture that condenses out of the air to flow

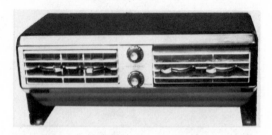

Fig. 2-12. Hang-on type evaporator.

out of the case and onto the road surface under the car. Often people think their vehicle has sprung a leak and something is wrong when they stop and notice water dripping from the vehicle. This condensate drainage is normal and indicates the system is working properly since one function of an air conditioner is to dehumidify the air.

The evaporator has no moving parts and is trouble-free except for the rare occasion when leaks develop within the tubing. This would occur if moisture were in the system and caused acidic action to eat away the evaporator tubes. If this is the case, the damage will be throughout the system and all leaking or damaged units will have to be replaced.

Condenser

The condenser is made of tubing, either steel or aluminum. Fins are attached to the tubes so as to have a large surface area to be able to contact and thus transfer heat to the air coming across the condenser. See Fig. 2-14. This air can be forced into the condenser by the forward motion of the car, or it may be air supplied by a fan or blower.

Air flow across the front of the car while it is in motion is called *ram air*. Ram air and the engine cooling system

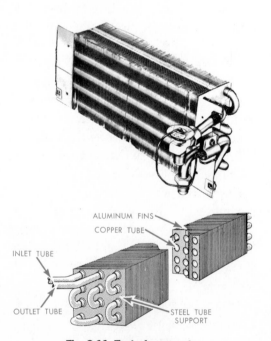

Fig. 2-11. Typical evaporator.

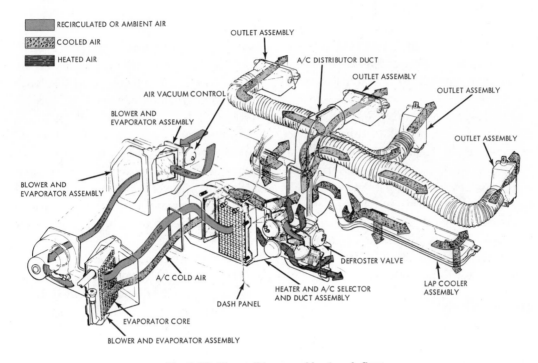

RECIRCULATED OR AMBIENT AIR

COOLED AIR

HEATED AIR

OUTLET ASSEMBLY

A/C DISTRIBUTOR DUCT

OUTLET ASSEMBLY

OUTLET ASSEMBLY

OUTLET ASSEMBLY

AIR VACUUM CONTROL

BLOWER AND
EVAPORATOR ASSEMBLY

BLOWER AND
EVAPORATOR ASSEMBLY

AMBIENT AIR

A/C COLD AIR

DEFROSTER VALVE

DASH PANEL

HEATER AND A/C SELECTOR
AND DUCT ASSEMBLY

LAP COOLER
ASSEMBLY

EVAPORATOR CORE

BLOWER AND EVAPORATOR ASSEMBLY

Fig. 2-13. Air conditioner and heater air flow.

Fig. 2-14. Typical double-pass condenser.

fan work together to keep an adequate amount of air flowing across the condenser.

Because of its location in front of the car radiator, the condenser is particularly susceptible to bugs, dirt and other road debris. If partially clogged by dirt or other obstructions, the condenser will not be able to provide the condensing effect necessary for proper air-conditioning operation. At the same time, engine overheating might occur because air passes the condenser first and then the radiator.

A condenser is also prone to front-end damage if it is located up front of the engine block. Aside from keeping the condenser mounted securely to eliminate vibrations which cause leaks, an occasional cleaning with cool water and a brush is the only service needed. If the condenser develops a leak, sometimes it is possible for a radiator repair specialist to fix it. If a leak cannot be repaired, the condenser must be replaced. Remember, the condenser must withstand pressures of 400 to 500 psi at times. It must be leak tight. Normal condenser pressures range between 150 and 300 psi during operation.

Condenser size is often limited by installation dimensions. The tubes can be arranged in a single, double, or even triple-pass fashion. This would provide more gas flow through a relatively small condenser configuration. A single-pass condenser is least desirable because it contains a very small amount of refrigerant. Fig. 2-14 illustrates the typical double-pass tubing arrangement.

Expansion Valve

All air conditioners use expansion valves to control the flow of liquid refrigerant into the evaporators. See Fig. 2-15.

Ideally the expansion valve will keep the evaporator temperature at 32°F at all times. (Temperatures lower than 32°F would cause the moisture present in the air to condense and form ice on the evaporator fins; this reduces cooling considerably.) If the evaporator is kept at its maximum cooling temperature, the expansion valve is performing as it should. Water which condenses on the evaporator will wash off dust and pollen and will be able to drain to the road surface through openings or tubes provided for that purpose.

The expansion valve is always located at the inlet to the evaporator. It will always have high pressure *liquid* R-12 at the inlet. The valve admits this liquid into the evaporator slowly. As this occurs the pressure is severely reduced as evaporator pressure is relatively low.

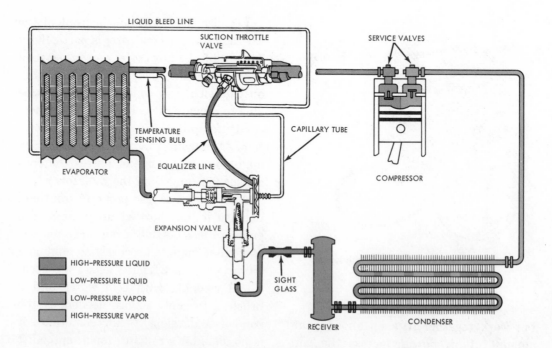

Fig. 2-15. Position of expansion valve in typical refrigeration circuit.

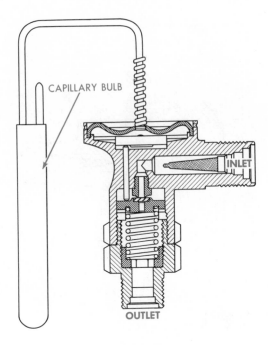

CAPILLARY BULB

INLET

OUTLET

Fig. 2-16. Expansion valve.

Generally an operating evaporator pressure of 15 to 30 pounds is normal.

With pressure reduced, the liquid R-12 then can boil rapidly, absorbing heat from air passing over the tubes and fins of the evaporator. When this vapor reaches the outlet of the evaporator, the pressure will be increased because of the heat absorbed. This increase in temperature is called *superheat*.

The expansion valve is designed to sense the temperature of the vapors flowing out of the evaporator. A sensing bulb is attached to the outlet or tail pipe of the evaporator. This bulb is usually partially filled with R-12. It is then connected with a very small tube to the top of the operating diaphragm at the expansion valve. See Figs. 2-16 and 2-17.

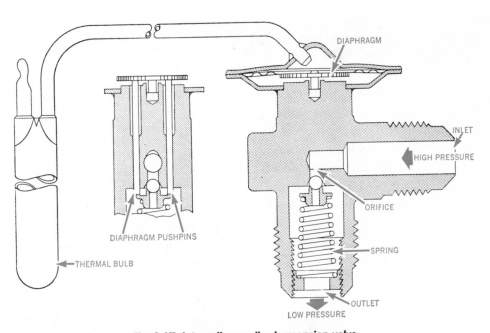

DIAPHRAGM

INLET

HIGH PRESSURE

ORIFICE

DIAPHRAGM PUSHPINS

SPRING

THERMAL BULB

OUTLET

LOW PRESSURE

Fig. 2-17. Internally equalized expansion valve.

The valve is designed so that when the temperature at the evaporator tail pipe is high (warm) it will open fully admitting a maximum amount of coolant.

The valve is opened because R-12 pressure from the sensing bulb is acting on the diaphragm end of the valve stem and is compressing the spring in the valve so as to cause it to open. The tension of the expansion valve spring is set for a specific amount of superheat. Usually this setting will be 8 to 10 pounds of pressure. This means that, when the vapors leaving the evaporator are 8 to 10 degrees *warmer* than the gases within the evaporator, the valve will open admitting more liquid into the evaporator. As the evaporator becomes cooler during operation, the bulb senses the lower (cooler) temperature and reduces the pressure on the diaphragm, allowing the spring to begin closing the valve. The expansion valve is not normally adjustable and must be replaced if found to be defective. Some older valves are adjustable.

A thermostatic expansion valve (TXV) is described as the *internally* equalized type of expansion valve in Fig. 2-17. The pressure under the diaphragm is internal evaporator pressure. Differences in inlet and outlet pressures are not normally strong enough to inhibit valve operation. However, with larger evaporators, an *externally* equalized TXV is used. The pressure difference from inside to outside can be high enough (3 to 4 pounds) to prevent control of the valve. To keep this pressure difference from adversely affecting operations, the underside of the TXV diaphragm is connected by a small tube attached to the tailpipe of the evaporator. See Figs. 2-18 and 2-19. This allows the

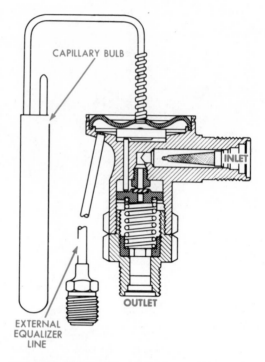

Fig. 2-18. Externally equalized expansion valve. (Chevrolet Div., General Motors Corp.)

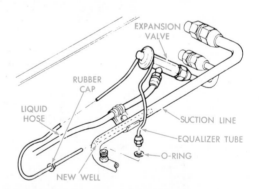

Fig. 2-19. Expansion valve details. Note that sensing tube fits into a well. (Chrysler Corp.)

valve to sense more accurately the needs of the evaporator by sensing outlet *temperature* and *pressure* at the TXV diaphragm.

Without this pressure equalization, the TXV could admit too much refrigerant, thereby flooding the evaporator and reducing room for the liquid to vaporize.

When the evaporator is flooded with excess R-12, poor cooling results, because the excess liquid is not able to fully vaporize.

The larger evaporator will have a higher tailpipe pressure and temperature than a small evaporator since most refrigerant flowing would absorb more heat. Thus, an evaporator might be operating well, but if the TXV is not equalized, it will cause too much liquid to be admitted, thereby flooding the evaporator. A flooded evaporator is one which contains too much liquid. The excess liquid has inadequate room to vaporize, or boil, which results in poor cooling.

Ordinarily, if not equalized, the higher outlet temperature would cause the expansion valve to open, when actually it should not open. This poor control of refrigerant flow leads to poor cooling. The equalizer prevents this and provides finer flow control on larger evaporators.

Some Ford Motor Company vehicles use expansion valves which operate as described but which differ in appearance. In particular, this type of expansion valve has no thermal sensing bulb. It is commonly referred to as the H-type valve. Note in Fig. 2-20 that the valve is a solid block of brass or aluminum. It has a metal operating diaphragm attached to this block. This diaphragm operates the valve to regulate refrigerant flow. Also, note that the inlet and outlet lines are all contained within the valve itself. This valve is attached to the evaporator inlet and outlet lines, with the refrigerant lines attached at the opposite side. The gas pressure in the evaporator outlet develops the operating force, causing the flexible diaphragm to move. No capillary or thermal bulb is used with this type valve. A

Fig. 2-20. H-type expansion valve.

fixed charge of gas and liquid is provided above the diaphragm to give a reaction force, along with spring pressure, to cause the valve to operate.

Expansion valves often present problems in an air-conditioning system. Generally, poor cooling will result if an expansion valve is malfunctioning. A pressure test of the system will help determine if the valve is at fault. Very low or very high, low-side pressures often indicate a defective expansion valve. Low-side pressure is the R-12 pressure between the evaporator and the compressor suction inlet. A valve which is frosted over is also not regulating properly, because it is not allowing liquid to pass. A valve which is stuck closed will produce very low, low-side pressures and could even develop a vacuum on the low side.

When the expansion valve is operating, the evaporator should be providing maximum cooling without ice forming. To provide control of temperature and to prevent ice from forming, a thermostat or icing switch is used. Refrigeration controls will be discussed later.

Receiver-Drier

The receiver-drier, or dehydrator, is a small steel can which acts as a reservoir for extra R-12 and also contains a small quantity of moisture absorbing material called a *desiccant*. Either silica gel or calcium sulfate is used as a desiccant with R-12.

The purpose of the drying agent is to absorb any moisture that might be in the system or in the refrigerant itself. The desiccant does not hold a large amount of moisture. One or two drops of water would be an example of the small amount of moisture the drier could absorb. Any

more water will form acid and eat away at the components. Even if a system is serviced properly, a small amount of moisture could create acid sludge and eventual failure of the system could result. Water could also freeze at the expansion valve, thereby blocking refrigerant flow. From these examples one can see that moisture is the most troublesome factor in all air conditioning.

Another problem that affects the receiver-drier is that any condensed liquid will drop to the bottom of the receiver-drier. Since the construction of the receiver-drier is such that liquid refrigerant is delivered to the expansion valve from the bottom of the receiver, any condensed water there will also enter the system, as is clear from a study of Fig. 2-21.

A receiver-drier cannot be serviced. If a component has been replaced or a major leak repaired, the receiver-drier should also be replaced to insure satisfactory operation of the system. If no leaks occur and the system operates well, the receiver-drier need not be touched.

The receiver-drier contains a filter screen and may have a glass plug on the top which is used to observe the refrigerant flowing past that point. See Fig. 2-22. This sight glass is not always on the receiver-drier. Many times it is at the expansion valve inlet or in the liquid line from the condenser outlet to the expansion valve inlet or in the liquid line from the condenser to the expansion valve.

If a sight glass appears to be clear, with no bubbles or foam visible, and the system is cooling, the indication is that the system is fully charged. Bubbles and foamy refrigerant can indicate either a low charge, or air in the system. If the glass is clear, the compressor running,

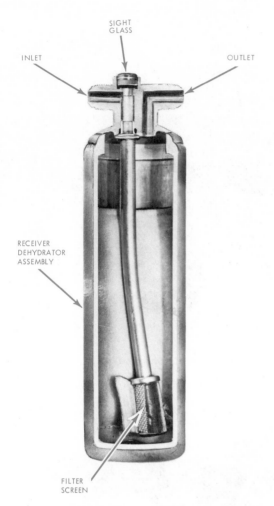

Fig. 2-21. Receiver-drier. (Buick Div., General Motors Corp.)

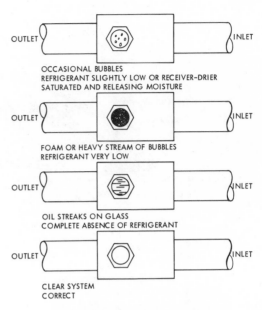

SIGHT GLASS INDICATIONS

OCCASIONAL BUBBLES
REFRIGERANT SLIGHTLY LOW OR RECEIVER-DRIER
SATURATED AND RELEASING MOISTURE

FOAM OR HEAVY STREAM OF BUBBLES
REFRIGERANT VERY LOW

OIL STREAKS ON GLASS
COMPLETE ABSENCE OF REFRIGERANT

CLEAR SYSTEM
CORRECT

Fig. 2-22. Sight glass indications.

and no cooling is apparent, the system has lost its charge. A test should be made to locate the leak.

It is possible for the receiver to become plugged due to the dessicant becoming displaced or because of dirt and sludge that have been left in the system or that have developed during operation. If the filter is plugged, the drier needs to be replaced.

The drier can be checked while the system is running by feeling with your fingers over its length. It should feel uniformly warm as it contains high pressure liquid R-12. If any cool spots are felt, this is an indication of a restriction inside. The restriction tends to act much like an expansion valve. The pressure drop across the restriction allows the refrigerant to boil which will cause heat to be absorbed. The next move is to replace the receiver. (This technique is also used to check for restrictions over the total system.)

Filters

Small screen-type filters are used at three locations: the inlet of the expansion valve, the compressor inlet, and in the receiver-drier outlet. It is possible for any one of these filters to become plugged and thus stop or restrict refrigerant gas flow. The only way to determine if a filter is plugged is to visually inspect it. Since the filter in the receiver-drier cannot be removed, if one is suspicious of it the receiver-drier should be replaced.

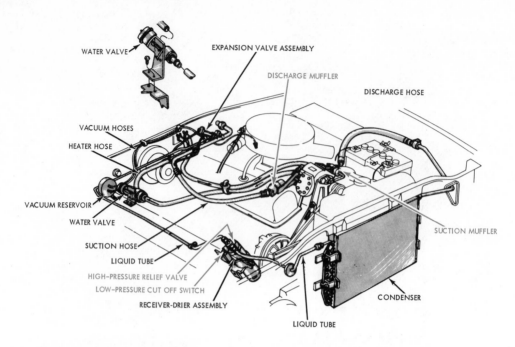

Fig. 2-23. Air-conditioning system with mufflers utilized. (Chrysler Corp.)

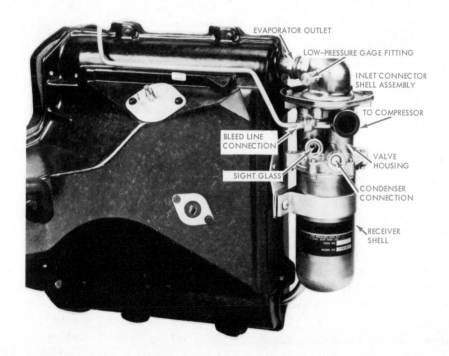

Fig. 2-24. Valves-in-receiver as installed on the evaporator. (Oldsmobile Div., General Motors Corp.)

Mufflers

Many times an air conditioner will produce noises which are due to the gases flowing within the unit. When these noises are objectionable, a round metal can called a *muffler* is used to dampen out the slugging gas sounds. Mufflers will be found on the inlet and outlet of the compressor. See Fig. 2-23. Some are relatively small in length while others are quite large. Size in diameter is about three inches and length from 4 to 12 inches. Short refrigerant lines can also be noisy. Often such noise can be eliminated by lengthening the lines.

Sharp bends and turns should be avoided with refrigerant lines as the sharp turns tend to slow down and then speed up the flow of gases. This can also cause noisy operation.

Valves-in-Receiver (VIR)

The *valves-in-receiver* combines the expansion valve, the receiver-drier, a sight glass, and an evaporator pressure-regulator valve (POA) into one unit. See Fig. 2-24. The VIR is mounted on the case of the evaporator. The expansion valve uses no thermal sensing bulb because the power element is exposed directly to refrigerant vapors leaving the evaporator. Fig. 2-25 shows the expansion valve in section. This expansion valve is equalized also with a drilled hole between the expansion valve and the pressure-regulator valve (POA) in the main housing.

It is possible to replace the desiccant bag, expansion valve, or pressure-regulator valve by disassembling the unit after all refrigerant pressure has been properly released. Chapter 5 will include more ser-

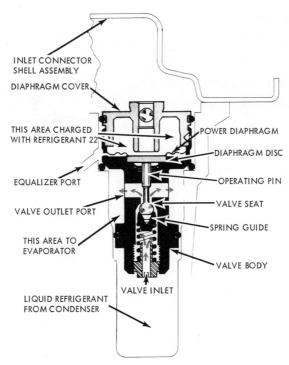

INLET CONNECTOR SHELL ASSEMBLY

DIAPHRAGM COVER

THIS AREA CHARGED WITH REFRIGERANT 22

EQUALIZER PORT

VALVE OUTLET PORT

THIS AREA TO EVAPORATOR

LIQUID REFRIGERANT FROM CONDENSER

POWER DIAPHRAGM

DIAPHRAGM DISC

OPERATING PIN

VALVE SEAT

SPRING GUIDE

VALVE BODY

VALVE INLET

Fig. 2-25. Section view of the expansion valve used in the VIR assembly. (Oldsmobile Div., General Motors Corp.)

vice details. Fig. 2-26 shows the position of the VIR unit with respect to other system components related to the receiver-drier.

The pressure-regulator valve (POA) mentioned above has not been explained, but in Chapter 3 the purpose of this type of valve will be explained.

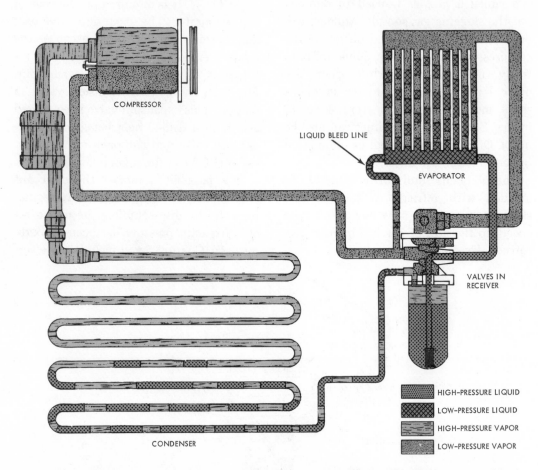

Fig. 2-26. Refrigeration system using the valves-in-receiver. (Oldsmobile Div., General Motors Corp.)

Special Features

Air-conditioning systems use a wide variety of special devices that are necessary to protect the system and its components.

One device is a high-pressure relief valve. It is usually located at the compressor high-pressure side. See Fig. 2-27. The purpose of the valve is to release

Fig. 2-27. Location of some high and low-pressure control devices. (Chrysler Corp.)

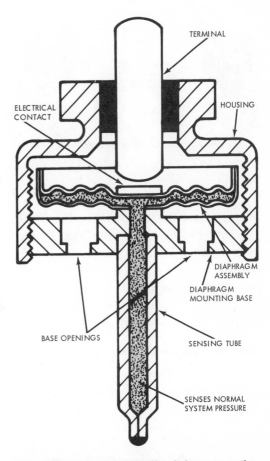

Fig. 2-28. Superheat shut-off switch cross section. (Chevrolet Div., General Motors Corp.)

pressure that has built up in excess of 400 psi within the system. By releasing this pressure, possible damage to components from too high a pressure is eliminated.

This relief valve is usually a spring-loaded valve which will close when pressure is reduced to below the setting of the valve.

Sometimes fusible plugs are used. These are located on the receiver and will melt when pressures and consequent high temperatures have developed. (A melted plug requires replacement and also correction of the high temperature condition.)

G.M. Superheat Switch

Other systems incorporate a switch on the high-pressure side of the system which is designed to keep the compressor from operating if system pressure is too low. Low pressure results if the refrigerant charge is lost. Compressor damage can occur under this condition.

The switch is electrical and is connected into the compressor clutch circuit.

Normal system pressure keeps the switch open, Fig. 2-28, and the compressor clutch will operate normally. When system pressure is low, the thermal switch will open the compressor clutch circuit thereby preventing the compressor from operating. When the superheat switch closes, it activates a thermal fuse and current will flow through an electrical resistance unit to ground. When this takes place, the fuse link will become hot and melt, breaking the circuit so the compressor clutch will not operate. The thermal limiter will need to be replaced

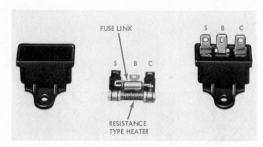

Fig. 2-29. Thermal limiter with superheat switch.

when its fuse has melted. See Fig. 2-29. Testing involves bypassing the limiter from terminal B to C. The clutch should operate. See Fig. 2-30. G.M. cars locate the superheat switch in the compressor, while other manufacturers place the switch at the receiver-drier.

Chrysler Compressor Protection

Chrysler Corporation uses a simple switch located on the receiver-drier which is closed except when pressure is low.

When the switch opens, the compressor clutch circuit is opened and the clutch will disengage. The switch can be bypassed with a jumper wire in order to test the system and make repairs.

Anti-Dieseling Relay

Some G.M. cars are equipped with an anti-dieseling relay. This relay keeps the compressor and blower on for a short interval after the ignition switch has been turned off. The purpose of the time delay shut-off is to utilize compressor drag to help stop the engine. This is necessary because of emission control changes which make shut-down of the hot engine difficult because of higher idle speeds. The relay is energized when the air conditioner is turned on and will not go off until the ignition switch has been turned off and the timed delay period expires (three to five seconds).

Occasionally a complaint may develop that the air conditioning is not shutting

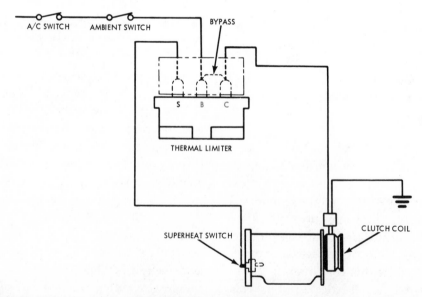

Fig. 2-30. Superheat switch with thermal limiter circuit. (Oldsmobile Div. General Motors Corp.)

off even when the control lever is in the off position. The anti-dieseling relay is the reason and there is no problem. Some vehicles with the anti-dieseling relay will also use a blocking relay. The blocking relay prevents blower operation. The blower will remain on for 3 to 5 seconds in conjunction with the compressor clutch if only the anti-dieseling relay is used.

Cooling System Modifications

The increased heat load imposed by the condenser is a problem which can affect the operation of the engine cooling system. To improve cooling system operation, several modifications are used when a vehicle is equipped with an air conditioner.

A large-capacity radiator is frequently necessary. A shroud which directs air flow over and past the radiator is also used to improve cooling. The air seal at the hood and grill area is also important for adequate air flow.

Some engines use a higher capacity water pump. An improved cooling fan is also helpful. Most vehicles will be equipped with a fan that has a higher air flow capacity than the standard equipment. This high-capacity fan will improve air flow considerably.

The high-capacity fan is most useful at low car speeds and is not really necessary as the vehicle road speed increases and ram air flow improves.

As engine speed increases, fan speed increases and this consumes extra engine power. Also the fan tends to become noisy.

To alleviate these problems, flexible stainless steel and fiberglass plastic fan blades may be used. The blades tend to reduce the pitch or angle of cut into the air streams at high speeds. This reduces air flow, power drain and noise. See Fig. 2-31.

THERMO CLUTCH FAN   POWER FLEX FAN   CROSS FAN

Fig. 2-31. Three types of fans used today; the cross fan is not used with an air conditioner unless it has five or seven blades. (Pontiac Div., General Motors Corp.)

Fig. 2-32. Fan clutch installed. (Ford Motor Co.)

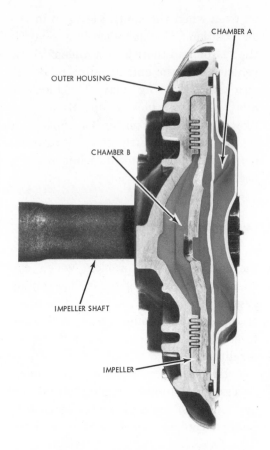

CHAMBER A

OUTER HOUSING

CHAMBER B

IMPELLER SHAFT

IMPELLER

Fig. 2-33. Sectional view of a viscous fan clutch. (Thompson Ramo Waldridge Co., Replacement Div.)

A viscous or fluid fan coupling, also called a *fan clutch*, Fig. 2-32, is a solution to air-conditioning cooling problems and is used on most vehicles equipped with air conditioning.

The viscous fan clutch uses oil between two members of the coupling. When the fan first starts rotating, the coupling, being stiff with cool oil, will turn the fan. As engine speed increases, the oil is warmed by friction and the coupling empties. This disengages the fan at cool driving temperatures.

As air temperature flowing into the fan area rises, a thermostatic spring reacts to the temperature increase and directs oil into the coupling providing a clutching action which causes the blades to turn, thus improving cooling air flow.

At high speeds the clutch is designed to slip, so it will normally operate only at lower car speeds when the engine is very warm.

Fig. 2-33 is a sectional view of a typical viscous fan clutch. Silicone fluid is able to move between chambers A and B. The engine belt turns the impeller. When fluid is in chamber B, a viscous drag is produced between the impeller and the housing. The housing then rotates, which turns the fan. The amount of fluid in Chamber B is usually regulated by a thermostatic coil spring or flat strip.

A non-thermostatic fan clutch does not have the control which is available when a thermostat is used. These non-thermostatic units are regulated by fluid tem-

Fig. 2-34. Two fan clutches. (Thompson Ramo Wal-dridge Co., Replacement Div.)

perature and built-in restricting orifices. Fig. 2-34 illustrates the two types of viscous units.

A quick check of the fluid-clutch drive is made by noting if a slight resistance to rotation is felt when the fan is turned by hand with the engine off and hot.

Frequently, if the bushings are worn or the oil has been lost, the fan clutch will need to be replaced. No service or adjustment is possible.

An electrically-driven auxiliary fan is also helpful to improve air flow across the condenser. Tight space and electrical motor cost so far have limited the use of electric cooling fans.

Since the cooling system tends to operate at higher temperatures when air conditioning is used, a high-pressure radiator cap is used to prevent boiling of the coolant. It is recommended that a year-round solution of water and permanent type anti-freeze be used when a vehicle is equipped with air conditioning.

Occasionally it might be necessary to install a slightly lower temperature thermostat to reduce overheating complaints.

It is important to recognize that an overheated cooling system will reduce air conditioning condensing effectiveness and also produce engine problems. When an older car is to be equipped with an air conditioner, all cooling system components should be in good operating condition to withstand the added stress imposed by the air-conditioning unit.

Problems to Consider

1. Locate the components which make up a basic air-conditioning system on three different vehicles. Report your findings.
2. Disassemble a compressor in order to become familiar with its construction. Have instructor check before reassembly.
3. Examine carefully how the thermal bulb for the expansion valve is secured to the evaporator tailpipe. Report your results.
4. Locate the service valves on three different air-conditioning systems. Identify high and low-side valves. Report your results.

5. Locate and report the types of evaporator drains you have seen.
6. Determine whether a condenser is single or double-pass construction. Report your findings.
7. Examine several sight glasses, observing what takes place when the unit is turned on and is turned off.
8. Report on any special devices, such as pressure-relief valves or mufflers, which you have observed on air-conditioned cars or trucks.

Trade Competency Check

1. What are the three types of air-conditioning compressors?
2. What types of valves are used in the automotive air-conditioner compressor?
3. Should compressor oil level be checked frequently? Why?
4. Describe the evaporator construction.
5. What is the usual location of the condenser?
6. What is meant by double-pass tubing arrangement?
7. What is the purpose of the expansion valve?
8. Where is the expansion valve located?
9. When the evaporator is warm, in what position will the expansion valve be?
10. What is the reason for using an externally-equalized expansion valve?
11. How does the expansion valve sense evaporator temperature?
12. What is the purpose of the receiver-drier?
13. What is a desiccant?
14. What is the purpose of a sight glass?
15. What is the effect of moisture in an air-conditioning system?
16. Where are refrigerant filters likely to be located?
17. Why are mufflers used on some systems?
18. Explain how the various types of pressure protection devices operate.
19. What are the advantages of the viscous fan clutch?

Operation of an Air Conditioning System

3

In this chapter the basic air distribution systems are presented along with several accessories which are frequently found on air-conditioned vehicles.

Methods of controlling temperature and air flow within the vehicle are discussed as well as the operation of the basic heater alone. Since more vehicles today are being equipped with factory installed air conditioners, the material in this chapter which concerns these units is particularly valuable to the automotive air conditioning specialist.

The fundamental principles as presented form a background of information which will make system trouble shooting and service problems easier to solve. A manufacturer's car shop manual used to supplement this background will then not only be useful but more easily interpreted.

Types of Air Conditioning Systems

Two basic types of air conditioning units are used today. The factory-installed unit, which is combined with the heater and referred to as the *integral type*, Fig. 3-1, and the air conditioning unit which is installed after the vehicle is produced, called the *hang-on type*, Fig. 3-2.

The refrigeration principles are identical for both types of units. The method of temperature control and air handling patterns are major differences. The factory-installed units use air from across the heater and evaporator to provide the operator with a temperature-controlled air flow. See Figs. 3-3 and 3-4.

The hang-on unit is controlled by a thermostat and does not utilize air from outside the vehicle. The thermostat is discussed in the section on Controls.

When an air-conditioning unit con-

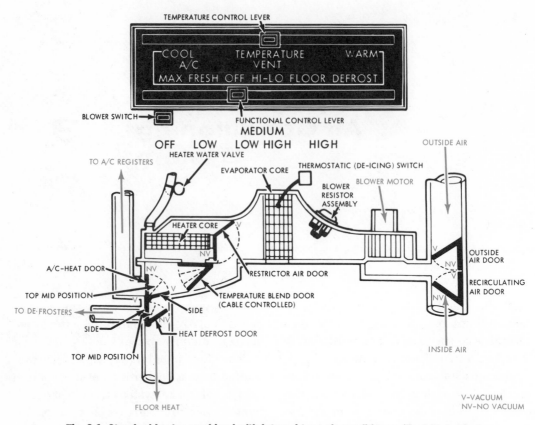

Fig. 3-1. Standard heater combined with integral type air conditioner. (Ford Motor Co.)

stantly cools the same air and does not bring in any fresh outside air, the system is said to be *recirculating* as using inside air only.

Factory-installed units can be set at maximum cooling which places that unit in a recirculating mode of operation. The hang-on unit is always a recirculating unit, unless a vent or window is opened to allow removal of inside air or addition of outside air.

Controls

A factory-installed, integral air conditioner will use a control panel that places the unit in the air conditioning mode or the heater mode which provides heated air only. In addition, the control head will switch the unit off completely. Most units also place the heater/air conditioning system in a *ventilation only* position which allows outside air to flow into the vehicle with no control of temperature. See Fig. 3-5.

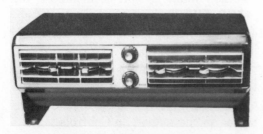

Fig. 3-2. Hang-on type air conditioner.

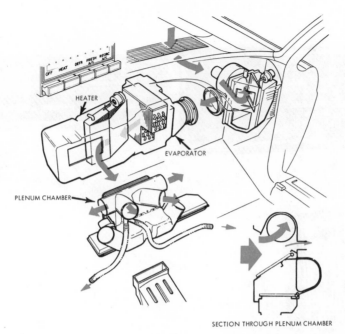

Fig. 3-3. Air flow in maximum cooling with outside air. (Ford Motor Co.)

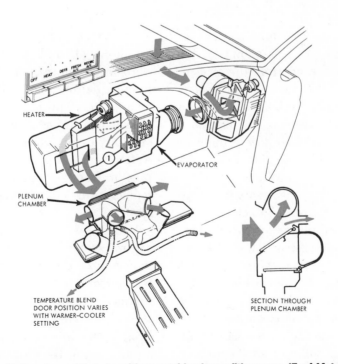

Fig. 3-4. Air flow in modulated position; outside air conditioner on. (Ford Motor Co.)

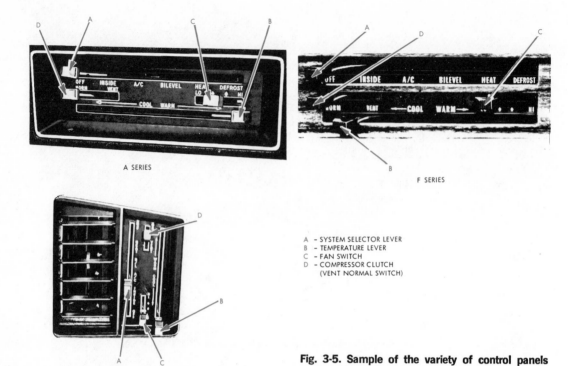

A - SYSTEM SELECTOR LEVER
B - TEMPERATURE LEVER
C - FAN SWITCH
D - COMPRESSOR CLUTCH
    (VENT NORMAL SWITCH)

Fig. 3-5. Sample of the variety of control panels used. (Pontiac Div., General Motors Corp.)

Certain systems also provide dual air flows for heated air. This allows for the discharge of heated air from the air conditioner outlets at the dashboard level as well as at the floor level. This is called a *Bi-Level* or *Hi-Lo* system. The heat position delivers the most air flow to the floor outlets, with a small air flow to the defroster outlets.

In cold weather it is necessary to deliver more air to the windshield to clear off fog and ice. Standard heater/air conditioners use a *defrost* or *de-ice* position on the control head to direct a maximum amount of warm air to the windshield defroster nozzles. This reduces the air flow from the floor outlets. The *air conditioning* or *fresh* position will cause the compressor to operate and direct the cool air flow out of the dash-level outlets.

Some factory-installed air conditioners are designed to allow the compressor to work in all control positions (air conditioning, defrost and de-ice) except *vent*, *off* and *heat*. This is a particularly advantageous feature as it will provide for dehumidifying of defrost or de-fog air flow. An ambient switch will prevent the compressor from operating, however, when temperatures outside the vehicle are below 37° F.

Vehicles with automatic temperature-control systems (Chapter 6) will use a *de-fog* and a *defrost* position on the master control head. In these systems, *de-fog* supplies some air to the windshield, but this air can be temperature regulated. That is, the driver could direct cool air on a warm day at the windshield if that were his desire. This would not normally be done, however. The *de-fog* position places the automatic unit in a heater mode with some air flow to the windshield. The *defrost* position on an automatic unit provides for a bypass of all cooling controls and places the system on maximum heat and highest blower speed for rapid windshield defrosting or de-icing. In *defrost*, approximately 85 percent of air flow is to the defroster nozzles, Fig. 3-6.

The defrost or *de-ice* position provides the driver with the greatest and fastest windshield defrosting.

A typical heater/air conditioner control will, when in the *air cooling* position, allow for fresh outside air to be brought into the vehicle as cooled fresh air. If, however, the control lever is moved to *maximum cooling* or *recirc* position, the system blocks off outside air flow into the vehicle and continuously recirculates the air within the vehicle. This tends to provide for a rapid cool-down of a hot interior. Frequently, the word *inside* is used instead of *recirc* on a control panel.

Many systems, when in the *maximum*

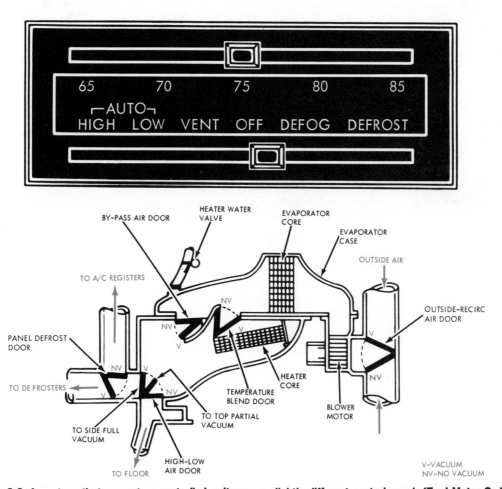

Fig. 3-6. An automatic temperature-controlled unit uses a slightly different control panel. (Ford Motor Co.)

cooling or *recirc* positions, do allow a small amount of fresh air to mix with the recirculated air. A small outside flow of about 10 to 20 percent fresh air is allowed on these vehicles by preventing the outside air door from fully closing. In *maximum* cooling or *recirc* positions a blower switch is used to provide different blower speeds. Normally three blower speeds are used. Some manufacturers now have no OFF blower switch position. In these designs, a low blower speed is on whenever the ignition switch is turned on, regardless of control lever position. This feature provides air movement at all times. Four blower speeds are available with this design.

When the driver-operated control functions are understood, the process of locating troubles is somewhat simplified.

Operating the controls and noting that air flows change according to designed patterns is a very good method of determining what is or is not operating properly.

Heater

Before a combination temperature control method can be discussed, it is necessary to explain how the heater of a vehicle operates. Note that outside air is forced by a blower to pass across a small-finned radiator. See Fig. 3-7. Engine coolant circulates through this small radiator. It is called the *heater core*. A heater hose car-

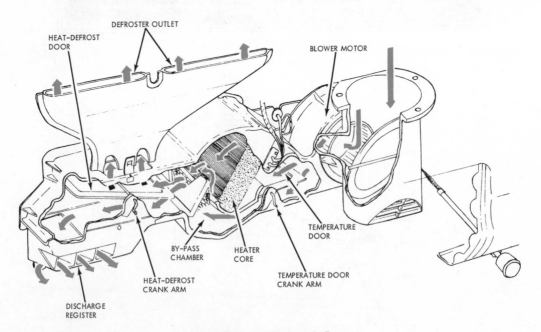

Fig. 3-7. Typical heater air flow.

ries hot water from the thermostat area into the heater core, and then it returns to the engine, usually to the water pump suction side. See Fig. 3-8.

As cool air passes across the heater core, heat from the coolant is picked up by the cool air and the warmed air is discharged into the vehicle passenger compartment. The thermodynamic law again is used . . . heat transfers to the cooler substance. Control of temperature is usually accomplished by diverting some part of the incoming air around the heater core. This diverter is called a *temperature door* or *blend door*. The driver positions the door for his temperature choice by moving a temperature lever on the control panel in the vehicle. See Fig. 3-9. Notice that for maximum heating all air is passed across the heater core.

For temperatures less than maximum, the door diverts as necessary, depending on outside air temperatures and the coolant temperature in the heater core. See Fig. 3-10.

Some heaters are temperature controlled through the use of a vacuum valve which admits more or less hot water into the heater core. A temperature door is not used on these systems. See Fig. 3-11.

Rear Seat Heater

Some manufacturers provide for a second heater core to be located at the rear of a larger vehicle. This secondary heater is provided with hoses which carry hot coolant from the engine cooling system to the heater core location. A separately controlled blower motor is used in conjunction with the heater core to force air across the core and thus heated air to the rear interior areas. See Fig. 3-12.

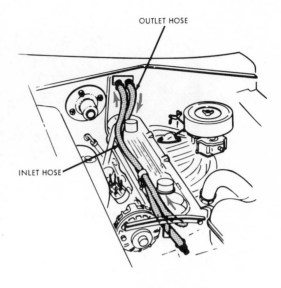

SIX CYLINDER ENGINE

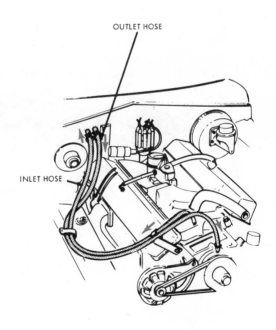

EIGHT CYLINDER ENGINE

Fig. 3-8. Heater hose routing. (Chrysler Corp.)

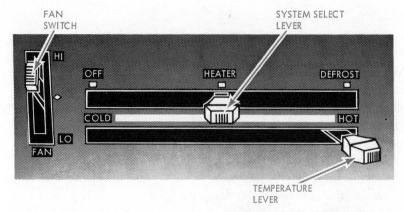

Fig. 3-9. A typical heater control panel. (Pontiac **Div., General Motors Corp.**)

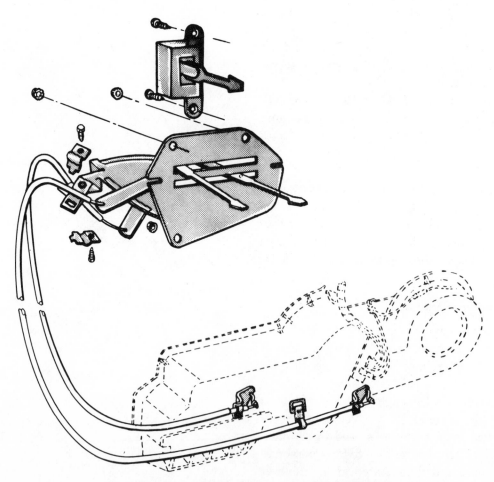

Fig. 3-10. Heater controls, cable operated. (Ford Motor Co.)

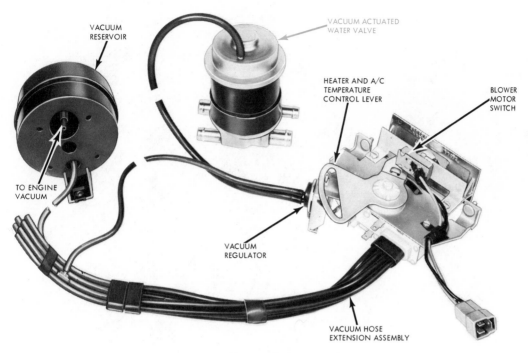

VACUUM
RESERVOIR

VACUUM ACTUATED
WATER VALVE

HEATER AND A/C
TEMPERATURE
CONTROL LEVER

BLOWER
MOTOR
SWITCH

TO ENGINE
VACUUM

VACUUM
REGULATOR

VACUUM HOSE
EXTENSION ASSEMBLY

Fig. 3-11. Vacuum controls. (Plymouth Div., Chrysler Corp.)

Rear Window De-fogger

An increasingly popular accessory is the rear window de-fogger. This unit is separately controlled and consists of a small blower motor which is installed on the package shelf of the rear window. This supplemental blower, when turned on by the driver, circulates interior air across the rear window to help keep it clear of moisture and to melt snow and ice which tend to accumulate.

Usually the rear de-foggers provide no heat but just an air flow. See Fig. 3-13.

Heated Back Window

Another method which is used to maintain rear window visibility in winter months is the heated back window. This is a method of keeping the glass warm enough to prevent freezing of snow or rain on the rear glass surface.

The heated back window is a specially constructed rear window which has embedded in it several small wires, connected to a driver control switch. When the circuit is on, the wires have enough electricity passing through them to warm up the glass surface, preventing ice from forming. See Fig. 3-14.

Figs. 3-14 and 3-15 show the methods used to control the electric current supplied to the heated rear window. The driver control switch is a three-position type which will return to the *normal* position after being moved to either ON or OFF. In the *normal* position, electric power is not able to pass the relay until the switch is moved to ON. Then the

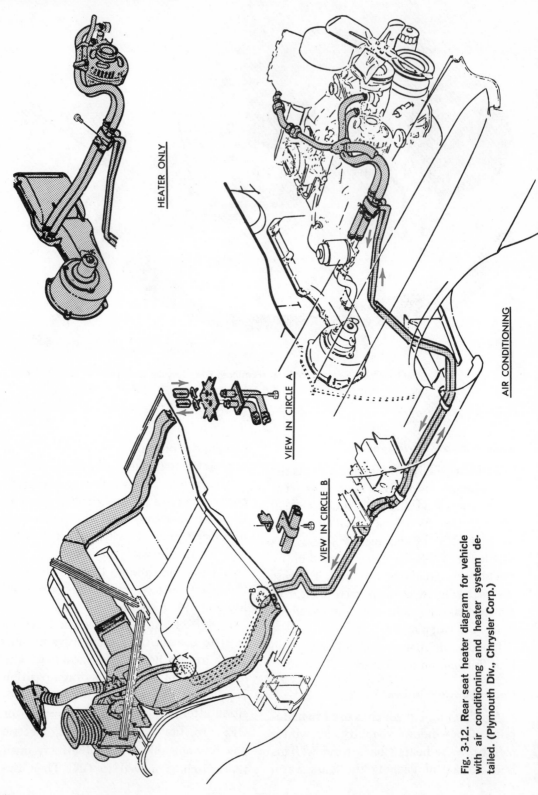

HEATER ONLY

AIR CONDITIONING

VIEW IN CIRCLE A

VIEW IN CIRCLE B

Fig. 3-12. Rear seat heater diagram for vehicle with air conditioning and heater system detailed. (Plymouth Div., Chrysler Corp.)

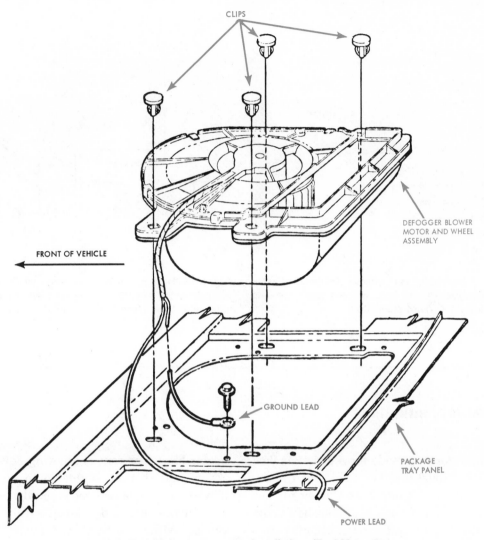

CLIPS

DEFOGGER BLOWER
MOTOR AND WHEEL
ASSEMBLY

FRONT OF VEHICLE

GROUND LEAD

PACKAGE
TRAY PANEL

POWER LEAD

Fig. 3-13. Typical de-fogger motor installation. (Ford Motor Co.)

relay closes and allows current to flow through the wires in the window to ground. An indicator bulb is turned on at this time. The released switch returns to the *normal* position and the window is heated continuously until the driver turns off the ignition switch or moves the control switch to the OFF position.

The holding resistor allows the relay to remain latched on until switched off. In a variation of this circuit, an electronic timer is utilized. The timer heats for a timed interval of from five to ten minutes and then shuts off the heating flow for another interval.

The rear seat heater, the rear window de-fogger, and the heated back window are very useful accessories and will be used on cars with conventional heater systems and on those with air-conditioning units also.

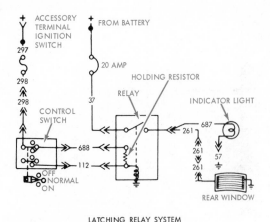

LATCHING RELAY SYSTEM

Fig. 3-14. Heated rear window circuit when relay is energized it will latch or hold itself on until switched off. (Ford Motor Co.)

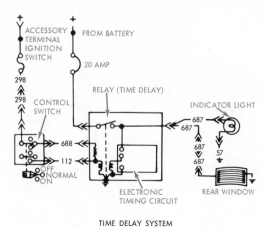

TIME DELAY SYSTEM

Fig. 3-15. Heated rear window circuit which uses a timer which turns the power off after a proper interval of time. (Ford Motor Co.)

Vehicle Ventilation

In order to provide for a constant flow of air throughout the interior of the vehicle, many manufacturers allow for the introduction of outside air through vents in the heater and air-conditioning systems. Improved air flow is provided when there is also a method of removing air from the interior of the vehicle, especially when all windows are closed.

Many vehicles use a pressure relief valve which is located in a rear door pillar which will allow air to flow out of the vehicle. Fig. 3-16 illustrates the manner in which the air flows to reach the pressure relief valve. It is necessary to remember that when all doors are closed and windows rolled up tightly, the body of most cars is tightly sealed. When the

heater blower or vent is allowing outside air in, and this air is unable to be removed, air flow is reduced somewhat and a slight pressure is developed within the vehicle. With the pressure relief valve, the air will be able to flow its rather unusual path under or over the rear seat into the trunk and then forward to the relief valve.

A few vehicles have been equipped with a vent which can be opened or closed by the driver. The vent switch is located at the dash panel. Operation of the switch would apply vacuum to a small vacuum servo, opening a vent located at the rear window area. This would then allow air from inside the vehicle to be exhausted while all windows are closed.

Outside air is normally brought into the

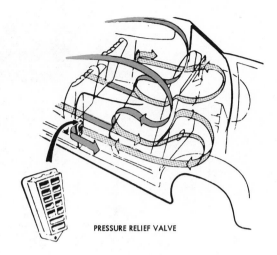

Fig. 3-16. Note how air is routed to reach the pressure-relief valve which is located in the rear door pillar. (Pontiac Div., General Motors Corp.)

PRESSURE RELIEF VALVE

vehicle at the lower windshield where an intake grill is located. The driver controls will operate a door which allows air to flow into the vehicle when desired. The door can be cable controlled or vacuum operated, depending on system design.

Vent arrangements are usually provided at the right and left front. Integral air-conditioning systems use the right air intake. The left side vent control is separate and normally cable controlled by the driver.

Combination Heater-Air Conditioner

The heater and air conditioner, when put in combination, work together by first cooling the incoming air and then re-heating it to achieve the selected temperature desired by the driver. See Fig. 3-1. This means that the evaporator will always be cooling at maximum levels and this cooled air will be re-heated by being passed partially across the heater core.

The temperature door directs the air flow just as in the heating system alone. The cool and warm air are mixed in an area inside the heater called the *plenum*.

This mixed air is then delivered into the vehicle by several ducts or passages provided by the design of the unit. For maximum cooling, the blend door will cause the cooled air to bypass the heater core. Normally, a water control valve is also used to stop hot coolant from circulating in the heater core during maximum cooling. This valve is usually vacuum controlled.

Generally, heated air only will be delivered to a floor outlet with a partial flow to defroster nozzles. When defrosting is

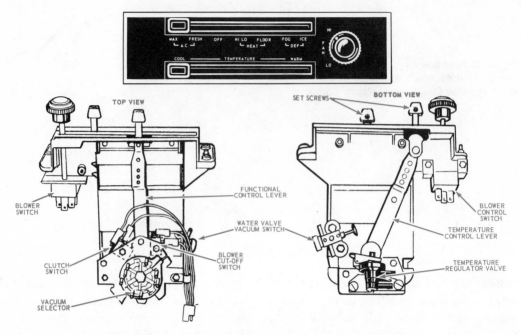

Fig. 3-17. Air conditioner and heater control unit. (Ford Motor Co.)

desired, more air is directed to the defroster passages and less air to the floor outlet. Warm air will mix with heavy, cooler air and will eventually rise up into the vehicle interior.

When cooling is desired, this air flow is partially switched. Cool air is discharged from several higher dash outlets where it can mix with warm interior air. Cool air will, because it is heavier than warm air, flow down to the floor area eventually.

These air flow patterns are controlled by the driver at the main control panel on the dash. The control unit acts as a master switch to open and close or otherwise position the various doors that direct or deflect air flow through the system. See Fig. 3-17. This air flow control can be operated by cables which would be mechanically operated by the driver at the

control. Another method of control uses vacuum motors or servos which open or close the doors with the application of vacuum which is controlled by a vacuum switch at the control head.

Frequently, a combination of mechanical and vacuum control is used. See Figs. 3-18 and 3-19. Typically, a system will use a vacuum-operated door to allow outside air to enter the unit. Also a vacuum door located at the lower right interior is used to allow recirculation of inside air only. Other vacuum servos operate doors to place the system in *heat, air conditioning* or *defrost.*

Many vehicles now also provide for heated or cooled air to be discharged at the dash outlets and the floor. This is sometimes called *Hi-Lo* or *Bi-Level* air flow. This provision actually allows heated air to be delivered from outlets which

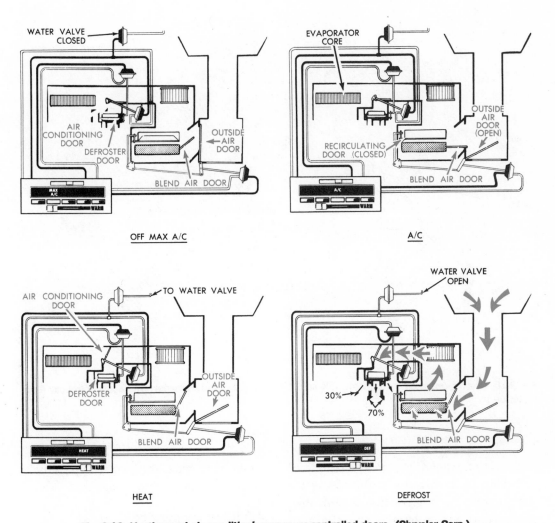

Fig. 3-18. Heating and air conditioning vacuum-controlled doors. (Chrysler Corp.)

usually are used for cooling only. Each vehicle will use these vacuum-operated doors to regulate air flow through the unit. The temperature blend door is either cable operated or vacuum controlled, depending on the system design.

Special Cooling Problems

Cool air, being heavier, requires a strong blower to be pushed out into the vehicle. A most difficult problem with which engineers are confronted is to try to keep front seat passengers at the same comfort level as rear seat passengers. In air-conditioned cars, the front area is cool and the rear is warmer. In a heated vehicle, the front area is heated adequately but rear passengers are cool in winter time. Air circulation and velocity need to be developed so as to provide total comfort for all passengers. This is not easy. Interior area, glass area, sunlight and the number of passengers are all factors which need to be considered.

57

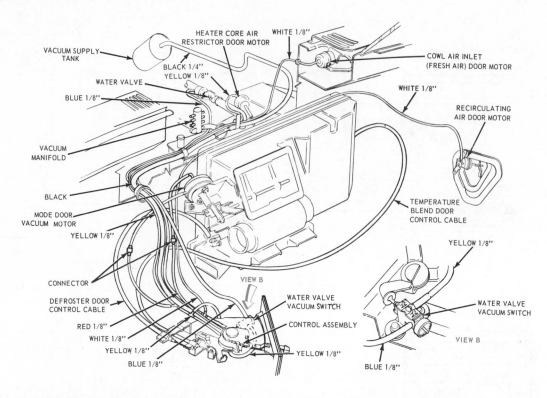

Fig. 3-19. Control operated by vacuum and cable; temperature and defroster are cable-controlled. (Ford Motor Co.)

A station wagon is a good example of the difficulty involved with providing total comfort. The front seat is comfortable, the second seat tolerable and the very back area is uncomfortable in comparison to the front. It is well to keep these factors in mind when a complaint of poor cooling or heating is heard.

Often the system is performing as well as it can but demand is much greater than the system is capable of handling.

Special Air Conditioning Units and Controls

Independent air conditioning units are also designed for special vehicles, espe-

cially van type and panel type trucks, and sometimes station wagons.

Auxiliary Evaporator

For instance, station wagons often can have an auxiliary evaporator installed at the rear of the wagon. See Fig. 3-20. An auxiliary fan then forces air across this evaporator surface to provide better cooling for the rear area of the wagon. Interior space limitations are also a serious problem. Small compact cars do not always have enough space for convenient mounting of the cooling unit at or under the dashboard area. Some designs place the cooling unit in between front bucket seats while others place the cooling unit

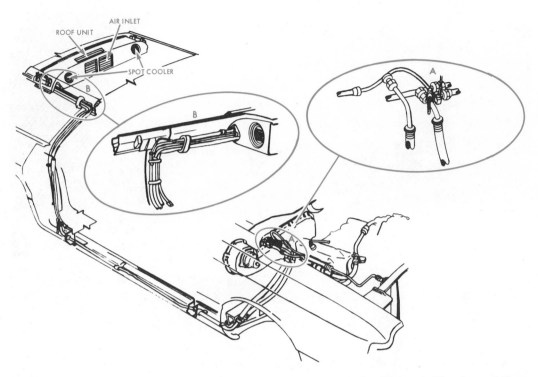

Fig. 3-20. Roof-unit, air-conditioning plumbing for station wagons only. (Plymouth Div., General Motors Corp.)

under the rear package shelf or even in the trunk. See Figs. 3-21, 3-22 and 3-23.

In addition to evaporator location, the placement of the condenser is a problem.

An air-cooled engine does not have a radiator, so the condenser needs to be positioned where it will have proper air flow

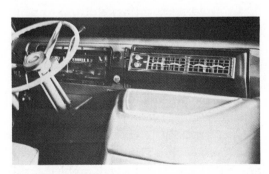

Fig. 3-21. Evaporator location for special vehicle —unit fits into dash. (ARA Manufacturing Co.)

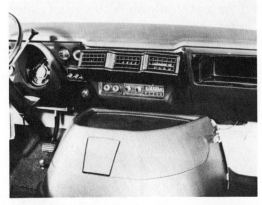

Fig. 3-22. Van-type vehicles can place evaporator in glove box. (ARA Manufacturing Co.)

Fig. 3-23. Air conditioner with evaporator located in trunk, outlets on package shelf; insert shows driver controls and dash panel. (Frigiking)

over it. Many trucks place the condenser on the roof of the cab, with a small motor operating a fan to provide the needed air flow. See Fig. 3-24. This reduces possible engine overheating problems that might develop if condenser heat were applied to the cooling system radiator.

Even in passenger car installations, overheating of the engine can occur because of the added heat load being applied to the radiator from the condenser. This is especially so during slow driving conditions, pulling of trailers, and long periods of idling. Air flow diminishes dur-

ing these circumstances and if fan speed is greatly reduced, engine cooling and air conditioner operation are impaired.

To avoid overheating, shifting to neutral and speeding up the engine sometimes helps. Keeping the engine's water pump and fan speed up is also beneficial. Occasionally, it might be necessary to shut off the air conditioner if overheating cannot be controlled in other ways.

Heat transfer is the task of the air-conditioning unit. Heat must be removed, and if it cannot be removed, problems will result.

Fig. 3-24. Condenser can be mounted on roof of vehicle. (ARA Manufacturing Co.)

Evaporator Icing Control

The evaporator icing control controls the compressor clutch of either factory-installed air conditioning units or hang-on units. It works differently in preventing system freeze-up. With cycling compressor units (in a cycling system), when a cycling type unit gets too cold (ice would form on the evaporator), the electrical power which causes the compressor clutch to operate is shut off. See Fig. 3-25. (With hang-on units, this shut-off is controlled by a thermostat.) Factory type units which cycle the compressor use an icing switch to shut it off. When the compressor is shut off, refrigerant flow stops and system pressures tend to equalize. This allows the evaporator to be warmed, thus melting any ice that may have started to form. After about a 7 to 10°F temperature increase, the compressor clutch is turned on again and the system operates once more. The operation of the icing switch is shown in Fig. 3-26.

The non-cycling type of automotive air conditioners involve a different method

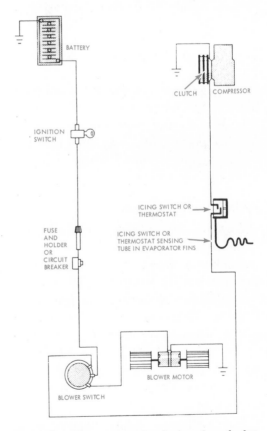

Fig. 3-25. When evaporator temperature is too cold, the thermostat or switch turns off the compressor.

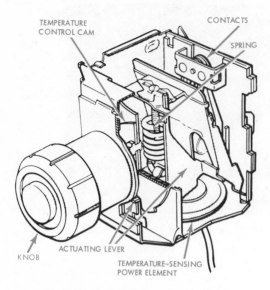

Fig. 3-26. Typical Thermostatic control.

to prevent ice from forming on the evaporator fins.

Some systems use special evaporator pressure regulating valves to keep evaporator temperature above but close to the freezing point. These systems allow the compressor to run at all times, thus it is a non-cycling system.

Cycling System Controls

A cycling system does not control evaporator pressure but uses an electrical control called a thermostat or icing switch to disconnect the compressor clutch when the evaporator temperature is near 30°F. When the compressor is off, cooling stops and the evaporator will warm up. Usually a 10°F temperature increase will cause the switch to turn on the compressor again and cooling would resume once more. This is a cycling system.

Note that when the compressor is off the blower circuit is still on, forcing air across the evaporator, so that the air flow

into the vehicle is not disturbed by the cycling system operation.

If ice did form or if humidity were unusually high, as the ice melts the air flow could actually deliver a misty spray into the vehicle. If this occurs, the driver should set the temperature lever slightly higher, or the icing switch might need to be adjusted to stop the compressor sooner to prevent icing. See Fig. 3-27.

Icing Switch or Thermostat

Note that the capillary sensing tube for the icing switch is inserted into the evaporator. See Figs. 3-28 and 3-29. This tube is then attached to a small, flexible metal diaphragm in the switch itself. Spring tension is attempting to open a set of electrical contacts. When the sensing tube is at 30°F, the gas pressure is reduced on the diaphragm and the spring snaps the points apart, thereby shutting off electrical power to the compressor clutch. As the evaporator warms, the sensing tube increases pressure on the diaphragm, which forces the contacts to close at about 35°-38°F.

An adjustment screw is located on the icing switch so that its operation can be adjusted as long as the tube and diaphragm are intact. A malfunctioning switch would be indicated when the compressor does not shut off and ice is observed on the evaporator fins, resulting in poor cooling. Early shut-off can be checked by using a jumper across the switch contacts. If the unit continues to run and cooling improves, the switch should be adjusted or replaced. The adjustment screw is usually designated with an indication of which direction to turn for colder operation.

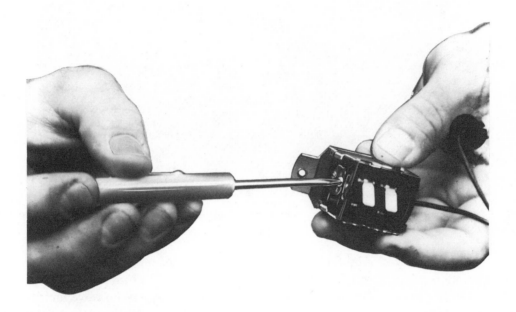

Fig. 3-27. Thermostatic switch adjustment. (Chevrolet Div., General Motors Corp.)

A hang-on unit uses a thermostat which is very similar to the icing switch. The major difference between the two is that the thermostat is adjustable while the icing switch is pre-set. When the driver

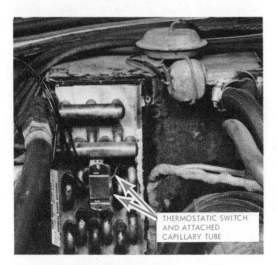

THERMOSTATIC SWITCH
AND ATTACHED
CAPILLARY TUBE

Fig. 3-28. Thermostatic or icing switch located in a factory-installed system. (Ford Motor Co.)

selects a cool position with his controls, he is adjusting spring tension so that the contacts will not open too soon. When a warmer temperature is desired, movement of the control adjusts the switch to allow the points to open sooner. See Fig. 3-30. Temperature is therefore controlled by turning the compressor on and off through the thermostat, as selected by the controls.

Non-Cycling System Controls

A non-cycling system is one which uses a special valve to control evaporator pressure to prevent ice formation. With a non-cycling system, the compressor clutch is always on when air cooling is desired. Since the compressor is always running, a means of preventing ice from forming on the evaporator is necessary. Two such devices are the EPR valve and the POA valve, Fig. 3-31.

Fig. 3-29. Icing switch located under hood; note also the expansion valve and the insulation around the temperature-sensing bulb.

The *Pilot Operated Absolute* (POA) valve is found primarily on General Motors products and in some Ford vehicles. The *Evaporator Pressure Regulator* (EPR) valve is used on Chrysler products. See Fig. 3-32. These are pneumatic controls.

The POA valve is located at the tailpipe of the evaporator and has a Schrader valve (like a bicycle tire valve) as part of its design for making test connections.

Both POA and EPR valves prevent the evaporator pressure from dropping so low as to allow ice to form. These valves limit

the amount of refrigerant the compressor can draw from the evaporator. In conjunction with the expansion valve limiting the flow of the refrigerant into the evaporator, the air conditioning unit of which it is a part should be able to provide maximum cooling with no icing. With this arrangement, there is no reason to shut off the compressor. These valves are not adjustable and must be replaced if pressures do not follow the manufacturer's specifications.

A liquid bleed line is used on a POA valve to insure that liquid R-12, which

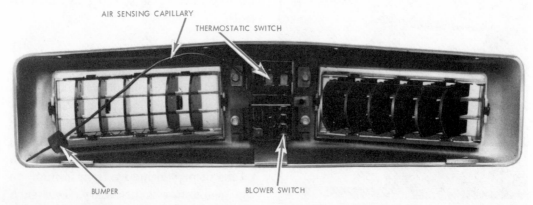

Fig. 3-30. Thermostatic switch capillary, located in evaporator air outlet. (Chevrolet Div., General Motors Corp.)

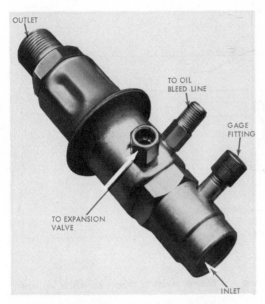

OUTLET

TO OIL
BLEED LINE

GAGE
FITTING

TO EXPANSION
VALVE

INLET

Fig. 3-31. Evaporator-pressure control valve (POA). (Chevrolet Div., General Motors Corp.)

Fig. 3-32. Evaporator pressure regulator valve (EPR). (Mark IV Air Conditioning Supplies.)

carries oil, will be continuously circulating. This provides for compressor lubrication when the POA valve is limiting R-12 flow.

On older cars, valves like the POA and EPR were called *suction throttling valves* or *hot gas by-pass.* They are not in common use today. Their purpose was to prevent ice from forming on the evaporator.

Related Electrical Controls

A simplified electrical circuit diagram of the controls of a cycling system is shown in Fig. 3-33. Note that the blower switch is the controlling terminal point in the circuit. When the blower switch is turned on, the blower operates, but current is also sent to a clutch switch and then to an icing switch and finally to the compressor clutch.

The clutch switch prevents the compressor from operating when no air conditioning is needed, such as when the heater or defroster only is wanted and the blower switch is turned on. Sometimes an ambient switch is used to prevent air conditioner operation in temperatures below 37°F. The blower switch directs electrical power to a blower resistor assembly which is located near the blower. By directing current to various resistance values, the blower motor operates at different speeds depending on the value of the resistance being used. Three and four blower speeds are available.

Many vehicles use a special relay which is turned on when the blower switch is in the highest speed position. This high blower relay sends battery power directly to the blower and bypasses the resistor block and blower switch. The high blower switch position energizes the high blower relay. See Fig. 3-34.

It is possible for a blower switch or the resistors to become defective. The high blower relay could also become defective. Operation of the switch and observation of variations in blower speeds will prove useful. The use of a jumper wire is also helpful in eliminating these units when trouble-shooting.

A blower that operates properly in all but the high blower speed would indicate

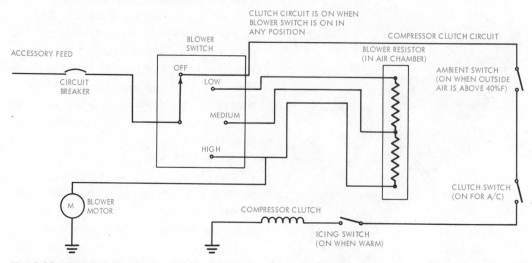

Fig. 3-33. Electrical circuit of compressor clutch controls and blower resistor; clutch switch is on when-ever blower switch is on.

a problem in the high blower relay, its fuse, or related wires. See Fig. 3-35.

When checking electrical problems, it is good practice to visually examine the wires and remove and replace push-on connectors to insure that corroded terminals are not the problem. A test light and jumper wire are helpful tools for checking these circuits.

The compressor clutch is one of the eas-

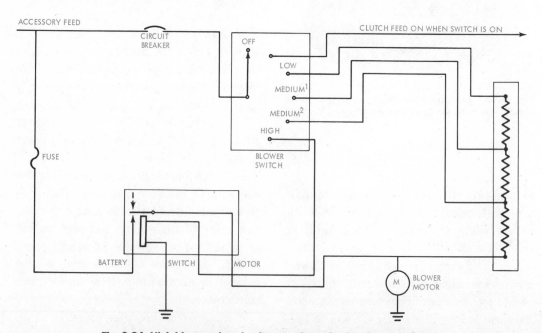

Fig. 3-34. High-blower relay circuit; note that relay is separately fused.

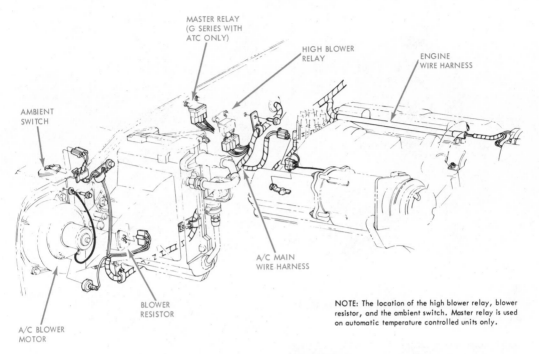

MASTER RELAY
(G SERIES WITH
ATC ONLY)

HIGH BLOWER
RELAY

ENGINE
WIRE HARNESS

AMBIENT
SWITCH

A/C MAIN
WIRE HARNESS

BLOWER
RESISTOR

A/C BLOWER
MOTOR

NOTE: The location of the high blower relay, blower resistor, and the ambient switch. Master relay is used on automatic temperature controlled units only.

Fig. 3-35. Underhood wiring.

iest units to check. If the compressor will not operate, a jumper wire from the battery to the clutch wire is used. If the clutch then operates, as evidenced by the clicking sound, the trouble is in this circuit. Check for power to and through the clutch switch, the icing switch and the blower switch; also the ambient switch if so equipped.

Compressor Clutch Operation

Compressor clutches are of the brushless, Fig. 3-36, or brush type, Fig. 3-37. Usually they are classified as rotating field or stationary field types. The stationary field coil uses no brushes and is most common. A rotating field coil would require brushes to deliver power to the moving field coil. See Fig. 3-38. If brushes are making good contact and the clutch doesn't operate with a jumper wire, the

clutch should be replaced.

A distinct clicking sound can be heard when the clutch engages the compressor to the drive pulley.

The compressor is electrically turned on by the magnetic clutch. When the

Fig. 3-36. Compressor with brushless-type electric clutch.

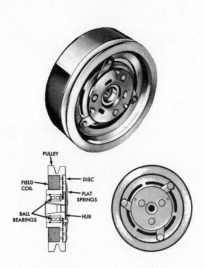

Fig. 3-37. Typical magnetic clutch; the brush-type magnetic coil rotates.

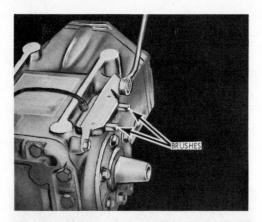

Fig. 3-38. Brushes used with brush-type electric clutch.

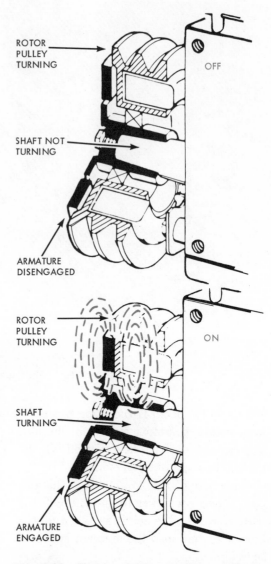

Fig. 3-39. Electric clutch operation; stationary magnetic field.

clutch is off, the compressor shaft is not turning, but the pulley is being rotated by the drive belt or belts. When electrical power is applied to the magnetic clutch coil, a flexible steel plate is made to contact a mating plate on the compressor crankshaft. This action starts the compressor operating. See Fig. 3-39.

Fig. 3-40 shows a typical wiring dia-gram for a factory air conditioner. Vacuum and electrical lines are both indicated. Because changes are made from year to year, this sample diagram should be used only if it applies to the proper vehicle year.

However, if some time is devoted to a thorough examination of the circuits used, it can be beneficial when a system requires trouble shooting.

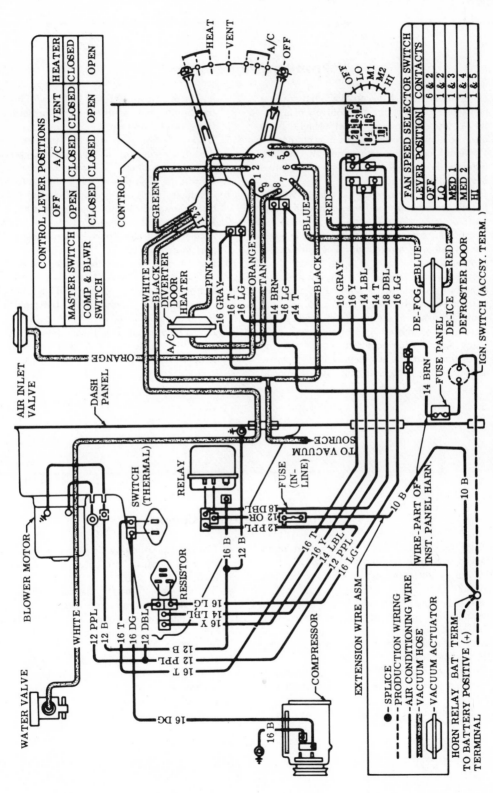

Fig. 3-40. Factory A/C vacuum and electric wiring. (Chevrolet Div., General Motors Corp.)

69

Problems to Consider

1. Observe and report the air flow changes you can sense by operating the controls of a factory-equipped air-conditioned vehicle. Note also the blower speeds and air flow changes.
2. By visual inspection determine how the temperature is controlled in several automotive heaters and air conditioners.
3. If conditions permit, use a vehicle with a heated rear window to observe how it operates.
4. Locate and trace the air flow path for a vehicle which uses a pressure relief valve in the door pillars.
5. Inspect several vehicles very closely to determine how outside air is allowed to enter; in particular, at the windshield area. Report your findings, and sketch the methods of directing air entrance.
6. Using several thermometers, check the interior temperatures at various locations within the vehicle. By changing blower speeds and temperature settings, you should be able to tabulate your results. What information do these results provide?
7. Inspect several A/C vehicles, and determine if they are cycling or non-cycling systems. How did you know?
8. Locate the high-blower relay and its fuse on a vehicle that is so equipped. If the fuse is burned out, what will the symptoms be?
9. Inspect several compressor clutches to determine if they are brushless or use brushes. Report your findings.
10. Inspect and observe the under hood A/C components on an A/C vehicle. Sketch the location and names of the A/C related devices. Include mechanical, electrical and vacuum components.
11. If you have a vehicle with a hang-on type air conditioner, determine how that unit controls temperature. Report your conclusions.

Trade Competency Check

1. What happens when a heater control is moved from *heat* position to *defrost*?
2. In air conditioning what does *recirculate* mean?
3. How is outside air warmed by the heater?
4. Explain how the reheat temperature control systems operate.
5. Why is it desirable to discharge cool air from the dashboard level?
6. Why is overheating of the cooling system a consideration with an air-conditioned vehicle?
7. What is meant by the term *cycling system*?
8. If a system is *non-cycling,* how is the evaporator temperature prevented from going too low?
9. Explain the difference between a *thermostatic switch* and an *icing switch.*
10. What is the purpose of an A/C clutch switch? Where does it fit into the electrical control circuit?
11. If a blower operates at all but the highest speed, what component is probably not operating properly?
12. How could you check to determine that a compressor clutch was operative?

Leak Testing Procedures and Trouble Shooting

4

Service and testing are very important parts of total automotive air conditioner work. This chapter presents the tools and techniques necessary to properly check automotive air conditioning systems. The use of the gage set is emphasized. When refrigeration testing is to be performed, this gage set is an extremely important tool to use in locating troubles or proving the system to be in good condition.

Gage Sets and Service Valves

The gage set is a valuable tool to be used when servicing and testing all automotive air conditioning systems. But before it can be used, we must know something of its service valves and remind ourselves of the precautions to be taken when handling R-12 refrigerant (pages 13 and 14).

Gage Sets

Gage sets used for automotive air conditioner service consist of two gages mounted on a special manifold. See Fig. 4-1. One of the gages is used for testing low side system pressures. The low-side gage is also a compound gage. It is termed *compound* because it will give pressure readings and also will read vacuum, which is very low pressure. This very low pressure is read in *inches of mercury* ("Hg). The low-side compound gage is normally located on the left side of the manifold unit. On the right side is found the high-pressure gage. This gage is not designed to read a vacuum and so it is not a compound gage.

The manifold to which both gages are attached is designed with valves and hose couplings which are needed to use the gages. In particular, it should be noted

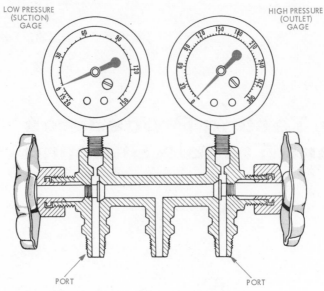

LOW PRESSURE
(SUCTION)
GAGE

HIGH PRESSURE
(OUTLET)
GAGE

PORT   PORT

Fig. 4-1. Manifold gage set. (Ford Motor Co.)

that there are three hose connections and two valves that are part of the manifold.

The gages are connected so that they will always register a pressure reading if a hose is attached to a pressure source. A pressure will register whether the mani-

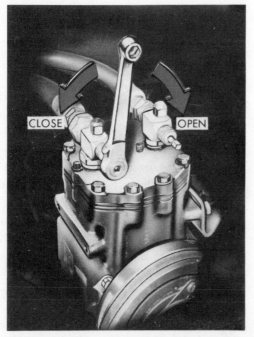

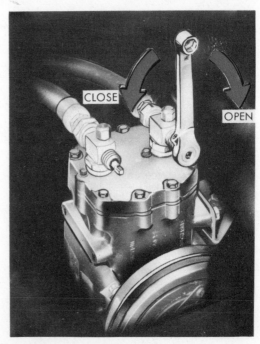

Fig. 4-2. Valve gage-port manual service valves. (Ford Motor Co.)

fold valve is opened or closed. Notice in Fig. 4-1 that the center passage is the only section which does not have pressure applied to it when the valves of the manifold are closed. The center hose is thus available to be used as a passage through which refrigerant can be released safely, or if the center hose is attached to a supply of R-12, it is possible to allow refrigerant to enter the system. This procedure will be discussed in more detail later in this chapter.

Service Valves

Before the gage set can be used, however, it is necessary to connect the gages to the air conditioner. To accomplish this, the connections need to be located; frequently, the connecting points will be found at the compressor itself.

The connections are made at valves which are called *service valves*. See Fig. 4-2. Since one gage is used to measure the pressure developed at the suction or low

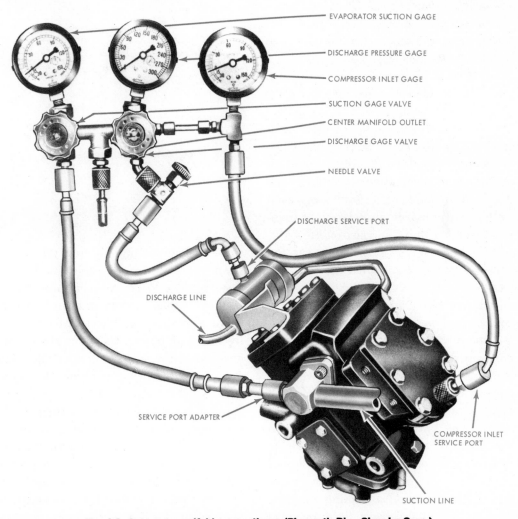

EVAPORATOR SUCTION GAGE

DISCHARGE PRESSURE GAGE

COMPRESSOR INLET GAGE

SUCTION GAGE VALVE

CENTER MANIFOLD OUTLET

DISCHARGE GAGE VALVE

NEEDLE VALVE

DISCHARGE SERVICE PORT

DISCHARGE LINE

SERVICE PORT ADAPTER

COMPRESSOR INLET SERVICE PORT

SUCTION LINE

Fig. 4-3. Gage set manifold connections. (Plymouth Div., Chrysler Corp.)

side of the system, a low-side service valve is located at the compressor inlet. If the low-side service valve is not located at the compressor, a search from the compressor back to the evaporator tailpipe should reveal the location of this valve.

The high-side service valve is located at the compressor discharge side. However, it is also frequently located in the high-pressure line to the condenser inlet. Again, if the service valve is not at the compressor, a search along the high-side lines should reveal it. Most systems use only two service valves, however some Chrysler Corporation cars are equipped with a third service valve to which an extra low-side gage should be attached, Fig. 4-3.

Service valves in use today are of two basic types. One is a manual ON-OFF valve and the other type is a spring-loaded Schrader valve, similar to the valve used in an automotive tire. The Schrader valve is the most popular and will be found on a majority of automotive air conditioners. The hand-operated service valve was used in the past primarily on hang-on or independent make units, and also on Ford Motor Company cars. The hand-operated valve is being replaced with the Schrader valve.

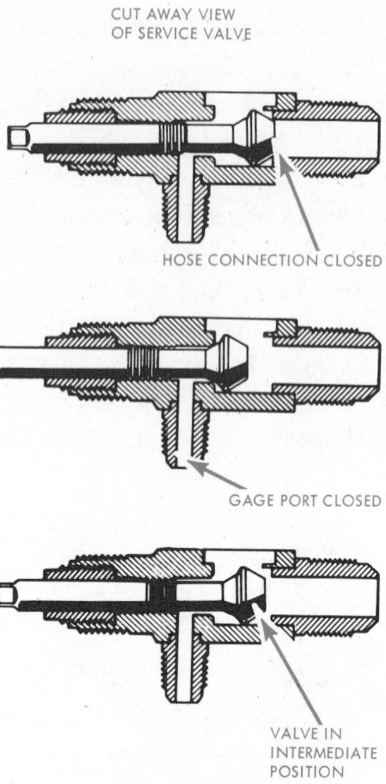

It is necessary to understand how to connect and use both types of valves. Fig. 4-4 shows a cutaway view of a typical hand operated valve. Since the high and low-pressure valves are identical, we need only to examine how one valve of each type operates.

Schrader Valve. A valve, when it is closed, is said to be *seated*. When a valve is opened so refrigerant will flow out of the valve, it is *cracked*. A Schrader valve is held closed (seated) by spring pressure. A protective cap is screwed onto the valve

CUT AWAY VIEW OF SERVICE VALVE

HOSE CONNECTION CLOSED

GAGE PORT CLOSED

VALVE IN INTERMEDIATE POSITION

Fig. 4-4. Manual service valves.

to keep it clean and to stop refrigerant from leaking out if the valve should leak. See Fig. 4-5. When the coupling from a gage set hose is screwed onto the Schrader valve, a small metal depressor in the service hose end pushes the valve stem down and causes the valve to crack open, Figs. 4-6 and 4-7. When this occurs, the pressure at the valve is then transmitted through the attached hose to the gage on the gage set. When the hose is removed, the valve then returns to its normal closed position. This is similar to inflating a tire with an air hose and inflating gage. The major difference is that the substance being measured is R-12 and not air pressure.

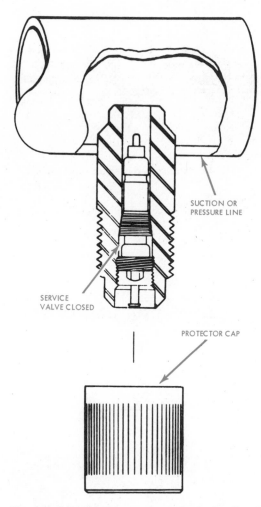

SUCTION OR
PRESSURE LINE

SERVICE
VALVE CLOSED

PROTECTOR CAP

Fig. 4-5. Schrader type service valve in its closed
or back-seated condition; note protective cap.
(Ford Motor Co.)

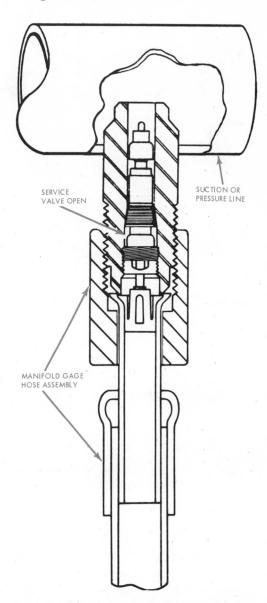

SERVICE
VALVE OPEN

SUCTION OR
PRESSURE LINE

MANIFOLD GAGE
HOSE ASSEMBLY

Fig. 4-6. A Schrader type valve in its cracked-open
position; notice that a gage hose is attached.

Manual Service Valve. The hand-operated service valve is somewhat more complicated but it is a little easier to work with. The hand-operated valve has a stem which is turned with a ¼″ square drive socket or a special service valve wrench. A special cap is used to protect the stem from damage and dirt.

The manual valve has three positions in which it can be placed. In normal op-

eration, the valve is fully back-seated as shown in Fig. 4-8. Note that in this normal operational position there is no pressure at the gage port. Thus the gage port cap can be removed and the hose from the test gage can be attached readily.

SEAL CAPS

VALVE CORE REPLACEMENTS IN KITS

VALVE CORE

Fig. 4-7. Fittings and replacement for Schrader valve. (Robinair Manufacturing Corp.)

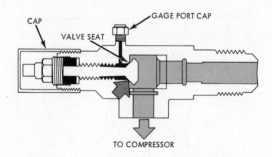

CAP
VALVE SEAT
GAGE PORT CAP
TO COMPRESSOR

Fig. 4-8. Back-seated position—operational.

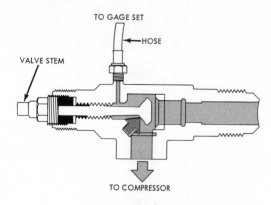

TO GAGE SET
HOSE
VALVE STEM
TO COMPRESSOR

Fig. 4-9. Midposition.

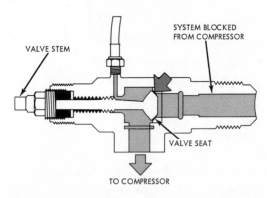

VALVE STEM
SYSTEM BLOCKED FROM COMPRESSOR
VALVE SEAT
TO COMPRESSOR

Fig. 4-10. Front-seated position—system blocked.

To allow testing of the system pressures, the valve must be manually turned with the wrench mentioned earlier, clockwise to crack or mid-position the valve. See Fig. 4-9. When pressure checks are complete, the valve is again back-seated, and the gage set hose can be removed.

The third position is called the front-seat. In the front-seat position, the valve stem is turned fully clockwise until it seats at the front of the valve. In this position, refrigerant flow past the valve is completely shut off. See Fig. 4-10. The advantage is that some service can be performed without the necessity of having to discharge all of the refrigerant from the system as is necessary when a

Schrader valve is used. As an example, if the compressor is found to be defective, a system with manual valves would allow removal of the compressor, losing only the charge in the compressor by fully front-seating the high and low-side

manual service valves which are normally located on the compressor itself. On systems using Schrader valves, the total refrigerant charge must be released before any gas handling component can be serviced.

Using Gage Sets

Practice with the connecting and disconnecting of Schrader valves or manual valves is the only way to fully understand how difficult it can be to master the task. The heat, pressure, and location of the valve make it a difficult job. It is necessary to hold the charging hose firmly with one hand and turn the nut with the other hand, with a rag or gloves covering the site. Experience is essential.

Attaching Gage Set

Practice using both types of valves is essential for the automotive air-conditioning service technician.

Removing a hose from the Schrader type valve can be very difficult because gas will leak so long as the depressor is contacting the valve stem. The procedure to alleviate this problem requires an understanding of how the depressor and

ATTACHING THE GAGE SET

CAUTION: Wear safety goggles. Use a clean rag or gloves to absorb refrigerant or oil

1. Locate service valves on the system
2. Remove gage caps slowly
3. Check that gage set valves are closed (clockwise)
4. Attach gage hoses to service valves
5. If unit is equipped with manual service valves, turn each valve clockwise about 1/4 turn
6. Gages should *both* indicate pressure: If no reading, system is empty; locate leak and repair
7. Purge air from hoses at this point:
   a. loosen hoses at gage set, let gas escape for about 3 seconds or
   b. with center hose open, release a small amount of gas from low and high sides by opening each gage valve slightly
8. Gage set is now ready for use
9. Start engine
10. Turn A/C on for *maximum* cooling, high blower speed
11. Set engine to idle at 1500 rpm
12. After system is stabilized (10-15 minutes) check pressures and observe sight glass

valve stem are operated. It will be necessary to press firmly on the hose to retain the sealed pressure *and at the same time* unscrew the nut which is holding the hose to the valve. A pair of cloth gloves or a shop towel is necessary to provide a good grip and to absorb any refrigerant and oil that will escape from the hose when it is finally disconnected. Naturally, the service man will wear goggles to protect his eyes.

The high pressure side will usually be the most difficult because of the pressure that is being released from the hose. The first attempts will seem to cause a large loss of gas. Actually, very little refrigerant is lost, and some will always leak out of the charging line hose itself.

It should be noted also that the manually-operated service valve creates little difficulty once the back-seat, mid-position, and front-seat terminology are understood.

Once the gage set is attached to the system the pressures are ready to be read at the gages.

Gage Valve Position. It is important to see how the hand valves on the manifold function. It should be pointed out that both gage set valves should *always* be closed when attaching or removing a test hose. On the gage test set there are three hoses, one each for the low side and high side. The third hose is used for charging, discharging and evacuating procedures.

Fig. 4-11 illustrates a gage set with two center service lines. One is used for charging—the other for discharging gas. One hose is all that is required. The two

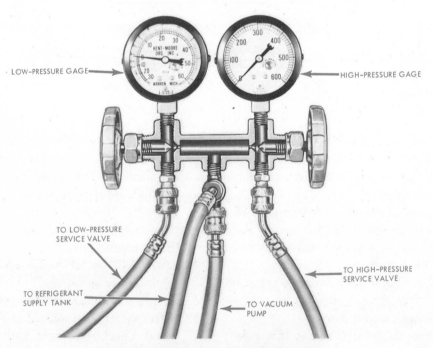

Fig. 4-11. Manifold gage set. (Ford Motor Co.)

hose arrangement is used with a charging station which is discussed at the end of this chapter.

Most Chrysler air-conditioning (A/C) systems will require the use of three gages for testing and charging. Although only two need to be used for charging and evacuation, the third gage is necessary for accurate performance testing. During operation, the high pressure pulsations received at the high-side gage are quite severe. These rapid needle fluctuations can cause damage to the gage and are difficult to read. A needle valve is used on the high-side gage hose to adjust the high pressure so as to allow for a steady gage reading. This is necessary when Schrader service valves are used. Manual service valves can be adjusted to produce a steady gage reading by turning back slightly until the gage reading is stable.

The third gage is a low-pressure gage which reads low side pressure. Fig. 4-12 shows a typical Chrysler vehicle hookup. Notice that a Schrader valve is located at the evaporator outlet just before the compressor. Another low side valve is on the compressor head and it tests compressor inlet pressure. The last gage connection is at the compressor discharge or high pressure area.

Note that when the valves on the manifold are closed, pressure on the high side and low side will be applied to the appropriate gage. Also note that if the low-side gage valve is opened, the low side is connected to the center passage and thus the center hose will have low-side pressure applied to it, see Fig. 4-13. If the low-side gage valve is closed and the high pressure valve is opened, the high-side pressure will be at the center hose. De-

pending on the type of service operation, one or the other valves will be used. However, it is extremely important to be sure the valves on the manifold are *closed* before the hoses are attached to an air conditioning unit.

Most good quality gage sets have provision for attaching or parking the unused hose ends when the manifold is not in use. This is very desirable because it keeps the hoses cleaner and tends to keep out moisture which could enter the air-conditioning system when the hoses are attached to the service valves. Always keep in mind that moisture, dirt, and air are very troublesome in a refrigeration system.

Purging the Hoses. When a gage set has been attached to the service valves, it is necessary to bleed or purge the lines of the air. This is done by simply loosening the hose nut *at the gage set* enough to allow a small amount of refrigerant to be passed through the hose, thus bleeding off any air that was in the hose before attachment to the service valve. A few seconds of refrigerant hissing or leaking out is all that is needed to purge the lines. Once a gage set has been attached, various tests can be performed quite easily to determine the condition of the system.

There is an alternate method of purging the hoses. Instead of loosening the hose-attaching nuts at the gage set, the air can be forced out the center hose by opening each gage valve for a few seconds and allowing the air to be bled out of the center discharge hose. It is important to make certain no air is allowed to enter the system. Air will contain moisture and dirt which may cause trouble.

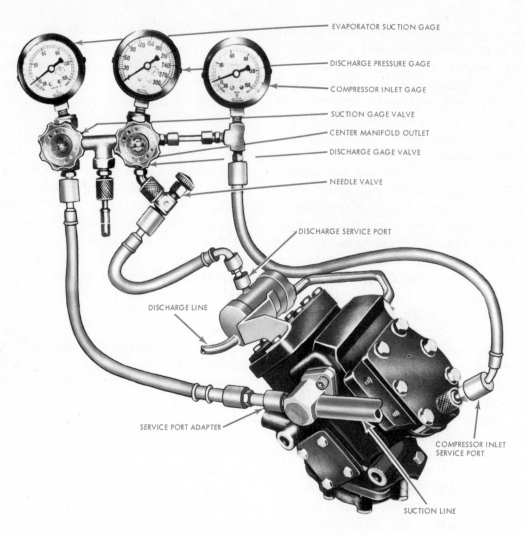

EVAPORATOR SUCTION GAGE

DISCHARGE PRESSURE GAGE

COMPRESSOR INLET GAGE

SUCTION GAGE VALVE

CENTER MANIFOLD OUTLET

DISCHARGE GAGE VALVE

NEEDLE VALVE

DISCHARGE SERVICE PORT

DISCHARGE LINE

SERVICE PORT ADAPTER

COMPRESSOR INLET
SERVICE PORT

SUCTION LINE

Fig. 4-12. Gage set manifold connections. (Plymouth Div., Chrysler Corp.)

Performance Test

The performance test is used to check the air conditioner to determine if it is operating properly. Before making the performance test, a thorough visual inspection should be made of the drive-belt, hoses, lines and other components. Locate and, if necessary, clean the sight glass so it will be easier to look into later in the test.

Do not test in direct sunlight. Always work in a shaded area. This reduces the heating effect of sunlight (radiant heat).

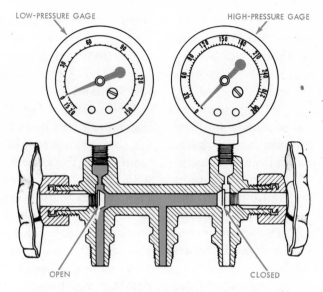

LOW-PRESSURE GAGE   HIGH-PRESSURE GAGE

OPEN   CLOSED

Fig. 4-13. Gage set suction valve open. (Ford Motor Co.)

INSPECTION GUIDE FOR
AIR CONDITIONING

A. Under Hood

1. Check compressor drive belt for tightness
2. Rotate compressor by hand
3. Locate sight glass
4. Locate service valves
5. Visually examine hoses, lines, condenser, receiver, for evidence of leaks (look for oily areas) or breaks
6. Inspect electrical and vacuum connections
7. Attach gage set:
   a. if pressure is 25 lb. or less add one pound of R-12 and locate leak
   b. if pressure is approximately ambient continue with performance test

B. Inside Vehicle

1. Familiarize yourself with control panel
2. Start engine (to supply vacuum)
3. Operate blower through all positions
4. Move control lever from position to position and note that air flow is correct
5. When A/C is selected the compressor clutch should be engaged if temperature (ambient) is above freezing
6. Adjust temperature control to maximum heat and maximum cooling. Note that temperature does change after engine is warmed up

If no obvious leaks or defects are noted during the inspection, the gage set should be attached to the appropriate service valves. Be sure the gage valves are both *closed*. Be sure to purge the hoses of air. If the system is empty, the gages will not show any pressure, or possibly a very low pressure. Proceed with caution if no pressure or low pressure is indicated. Remember that R-12 should reflect the system temperature with a pressure close to the temperature. One or two thermometers are needed to make this performance test. Two thermometers will make the job easier, but one can be used.

The engine should be started and set to run at 1500 to 2000 rpm. The choke fast-idle cam can be used to increase speed without upsetting the normal idle speed. Windows and doors should be closed. The air conditioner should be turned on for highest blower speed and maximum cooling. Allow the system to stabilize for ten to fifteen minutes. If no cooling takes place on start up, check the sight glass. If oily streaks are evident or many bubbles or foam appear in the sight glass, the system is empty or very low on charge. If the sight glass is clear and no cooling occurs, the system is probably empty of refrigerant. Gage pressures will probably be low also.

If this is the case, the engine should be stopped and preparation made to locate the source of the leak. The compressor could be damaged if run without refrigerant.

Assuming there is refrigerant, the next step is to measure the temperature of the air coming out of the discharge ducts as near to the evaporator as possible, but first be sure all windows and doors are closed. Note the temperature and then, using a thermometer, note the temperature of the air just in front of the condenser. With the two temperatures noted, a look at the gage set will give you the low side and high side pressures.

Interpreting Gage Pressures. As a general rule, the low-side pressure should fall somewhere between 10 to 35 psi, depending on the ambient conditions, Fig. 4-14. Outside air temperature, if very high, will make the system work hard and it may not develop as low a pressure as on a cooler day. This low-side pressure also indicates the approximate temperature in the evaporator. Because the temperature and pressure of R-12 are very nearly the same at low pressures, this is easy to check. If the low-side pressure is 30 psi, the evaporator temperature is very close to 30°F. A temperature-pressure chart can be used for more exact conversions. The high-side pressure reading should be noted. A normal high-side pressure will usually be double the air temperature at the condenser with a variation of plus or minus 20 pounds allowed. If the condenser air temperature were 90°F, the high-side pressure would be approximately 180 psi, ranging from 160 psi to 200 psi. As the air temperature goes up, so will the high-side pressure. This maintains a temperature differential at the condenser so that proper condensing of the hot gas back to hot liquid can take place. Check the sight glass. A clear sight glass indicates a full system if cooling is taking place. Otherwise, a clear sight glass indicates an empty system.

The next step is to disconnect the compressor clutch wire so as to stop the compressor. The purpose of this check is to determine if the system is overcharged with R-12. Observe the sight glass closely,

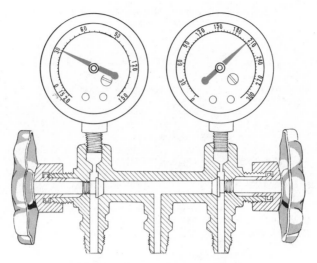

Fig. 4-14. Normal test pressures. (Ford Motor Co.)

when the clutch is disconnected, and watch for a stream of bubbles to flow by within one minute. If a slug of bubbles is seen within one minute, the system is not overcharged. If bubbles appear after a minute, then the system has too much charge of R-12. This would cause the high-side pressures to become unusually high also. Unusually high pressure can cause partial damage to the compressor, as it will be overworked.

To complete the performance test, check the controls in the vehicle for proper operation. The blower should respond with its different speeds, and air should be discharging from the proper outlets when set on *cooling*, and discharging at the defroster nozzles when on *defrost* position. After the system has been checked and all areas are satisfactory, the system is considered good and the test is completed.

Some car manufacturers supply tables

in their shop manuals for checking temperatures and pressures for their particular units, as illustrated in Tables 4-1 and 4-2. These should be referred to for further information on the performance data. If no tables are available, the above mentioned general rules will be satisfactory for almost all vehicles.

The discharge temperature of a hang-on unit will usually be lower than the factory integral units. This is so because the evaporator is positioned farther from the discharge outlets on the integral units. The air coming off the evaporator can pick up a considerable amount of heat before it is discharged into the vehicle. A hang-on unit places the evaporator in the vehicle proper, so lower discharge temperatures should be expected.

Let us now review the various steps of the performance test we have been following in the preceding pages.

TABLE 4-1 AIR CONDITIONER PERFORMANCE TABLE
G.M. SYSTEMS

TEMPERATURE OF AIR ENTERING CONDENSER	70°	80°	90°	100°	110°	120°
ENGINE RPM			2000			
COMPRESSOR HEAD PRESSURE	120–130	135–145	160–170	190–200	220–230	250–260
EVAPORATOR PRESSURE AT POA			28.5–29.5 PSI			
DISCHARGE AIR TEMPERATURE AT RIGHT HAND OUTLET	34–39	35–40	36–41	38–43	39–44	41–46

SYSTEM QUICK CHECKS

1. Check compressor belt tension, condition of belt and pulley alignment
2. Check clutch for energizing
3. Check for oil loss evidence under the hood, especially around the compressor shaft seal
4. Check electrical wires for wear, also vacuum hoses for cracks, splits, pinches and good connections
5. Check fan clutch, fan blades, radiator cap and permanent anti-freeze content
6. Clean condenser for good air flow
7. Connect manifold gages and hoses into system
8. Start engine and set air conditioning unit to *maximum*. Make note of pressures (high and low side). Make visual inspection of system through sight glass (bubbles are an indication of low charge)
9. Note discharge and condenser air temperature
10. Disconnect clutch for overcharge check
11. Check controls for air velocity
12. Check for proper air discharge
13. Slow down idle; disconnect test gages
14. Return to service or repair as test indicates

Leak Testing

If a leak is suspected as the cause of refrigerant loss, the leak must be located and repaired. A refrigerant leak will be indicated when oily spots are found along the path of the suspected area, as refrigerant leaks out it will also carry oil with it. Careful inspection alone will often locate the leak area.

To pinpoint the leak exactly, a test

TABLE 4-2 AIR CONDITIONER PERFORMANCE CHART
TYPICAL OF FORD CARS

RELATIVE HUMIDITY PERCENT	SURROUNDING AIR TEMPERATURE (° F)	ENGINE SPEED RPM	MAXIMUM DESIRABLE CENTER REGISTER DISCHARGE AIR TEMPERATURE (° F)	SUCTION PRESSURE PSI (REF)	HEAD PRESSURE PSI (+25 PSI)
20	70	1500	43	11	177
	80		48	15	208
	90		55	20	226
	100		63	23	255
30	70	1500	45	12	181
	80		51	16	214
	90		59	22	234
	100		67	26	267
40	70	1500	47	13	185
	80		54	18	220
	90		62	24	243
	100		72	29	278
50	70	1500	49	14	189
	80		57	19	226
	90		66	26	251
	100		77	32	289
60	70	1500	51	15	193
	80		60	21	233
	90		70	28	259
	100		82	35	300
70	70	1500	53	16	198
	80		63	22	238
	90		73	30	267
	100		88	37	312
80	70	1500	55	18	202
	80		65	24	244
	90		77	32	277
	100		-	-	-
90	70	1500	58	19	206
	80		68	25	250
	90		81	34	284
	100		-	-	-

charge is needed and a leak detector is used. See Fig. 4-15. A test charge is a charge of R-12 placed into the system so as to pressurize the components. The test charge involves using the manifold gage set and a small amount of refrigerant. Usually one pound will be enough to lo- cate most leaks. Then you can locate the leak source with a leak detector.

It is quite simple to put R-12 into the system, using the gage set. The center manifold hose is attached to a refrigerant source, the line is purged of air and with the air conditioning unit ON and com-

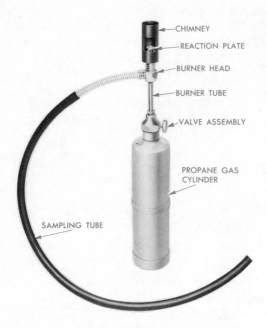

Fig. 4-15. Leak detector.

CHIMNEY
REACTION PLATE
BURNER HEAD
BURNER TUBE
VALVE ASSEMBLY
PROPANE GAS CYLINDER
SAMPLING TUBE

pressor running, the low-side valve can be opened slowly on the gage set. The higher pressure in the refrigerant container will force the R-12 into the system. If the compressor is not operating, refrigerant pressure alone is adequate to pressurize the unit for leak testing. A pressure of at least 80 psi should be developed on the high side before leak testing is begun.

Leak Detectors. Several types of leak detectors are used in automotive air conditioning service. Electronic and gas flame leak detectors are commonly used. The most popular and least expensive is the gas flame leak detector.

Fig. 4-15 shows a typical flame type leak detector. Leaks are detected by color changes which occur to the flame of the gas cylinder. Butane and propane are the type gases used.

A copper reaction plate and an aspirator hose are used. The hose is used to reach in areas where a leak is suspected. As the flame is burning, air is being drawn in through the hose. If refrigerant gas is passed across the copper reaction plate, the color of the flame will change to a *violet hue* if propane gas is used. Butane will change the flame color to a *greenish hue*.

Fig. 4-16 shows a smaller, more compact, gas-type leak detector. Since these detectors are designed to locate leaks by burning the leaking gas, it is important that this type detector be used in areas where ventilation is adequate. Remember that the refrigerant forms toxic halogen acids and phosgene gas when it is burned.

Electronic leak detectors use a small tube to sniff the air and incorporate a flashing neon light or a clicking sound to indicate the presence of refrigerant gases. See Fig. 4-17.

Often small leaks cannot be located with detectors. It is possible for the refrigerant to leak out when the system is cold and inoperative but not to leak when

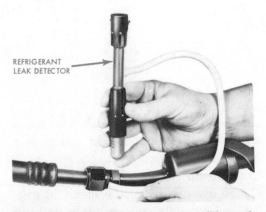

REFRIGERANT LEAK DETECTOR

Fig. 4-16. Refrigerant leak detector. (Plymouth Div. Chrysler Corp.)

Fig. 4-17. Electronic leak detector. (Robinair Manufacturing Corp.)

operating and warmed up. These cold leaks, as they are called, can sometimes be found by using a color dye in the system. The color would serve as a guide to the source of the leak. The dye is introduced with a small amount of refrigerant as in the test charge. Dye is often available in a refrigerant can, such as DuPont's Freon with Dytel.

Occasionally, areas are suspected of leaking and are not accessible to the detectors. A liquid soap solution can be used to locate these leaks if it is swabbed on over all connections and pipes. Bubbles will form at the leak.

The common places where leaks occur are the lines and fittings, compressor shaft seal, and the condenser tubing. Connectors logically are prime suspects for leaks. A burst hose or a chafed line are other types of conditions which are also found frequently. Usually a leak of any size can be located by visual inspection of these locations. A test procedure then can verify the leak site.

It is possible for pinhole size leaks to develop in the evaporator or the condenser tubing. These leaks are difficult to locate and usually would require replacement of the leaking component. Refrigerant will not be lost from a tight system. Some vehicles will maintain a full charge for five years with little loss. Still others operate well but need to be recharged once a year.

NOTE: It may be necessary in some cases to check under the vehicle. Also the removal of covering sheet metal may be required in order to locate all connections at the condenser.

If a leak is located, the system needs to be discharged so the leak can be repaired. Whenever any component needs to be repaired or replaced, the refrigerant charge in the unit must be released to remove all the pressure from the system. If manual valves are used, the compressor can be serviced without discharging the whole system.

LEAK TESTING GUIDE

1. Check system for obvious signs of a leak; look for oily spots near connections and at locations where lines and hoses pass through openings
2. Connect a gage set to the unit
3. If gages show 60-80 psi, the system can be checked with a leak detector
4. If gages show no pressure or very low readings, add one pound of refrigerant *with system off*
   a. Attach refrigerant supply can to center gage hose
   b. Open high-pressure gage valve and refrigerant supply valve
   c. Observe that refrigerant flows into system; gages should begin to show an increase in pressure
   d. If necessary, place refrigerant in warm water to increase flow into the unit
   e. Turn off both valves and proceed with leak detector
5. Using leak detector, search all connections, and the condenser, compressor, receiver and evaporator
6. To check the evaporator, place the blower on its lowest speed and search at the discharge openings for evidence of a gas leak
7. If a connection is leaking, tighten it and recheck
8. When other repairs are needed, the system will need to be discharged before disassembly and repair
9. If a leak is located and there is evidence of a large loss of oil, the compressor oil level should be checked; see instructions in Chapter 5

DISCHARGING THE SYSTEM

1. Attach gage set according to previous instructions
2. Place center hose of gage set into floor exhaust outlet or near floor in well-ventilated area
3. Open high-pressure gage valve slowly; refrigerant should be escaping out end of the center hose
4. Regulate flow of discharge so that very little oil is observed coming out of the center hose
5. Open low-side gage valve; regulate so as to control oil discharge also
6. When both gages register zero and no gas pressure can be felt within the center hose by your finger outside the hose, then the system can be serviced safely

Discharging the System

With a gage set connected as described earlier, discharging the system is very simple. But remember all CAUTIONS on handling refrigerants. The center hose is positioned near an exhaust outlet or near the floor. With the system off, the low and high-side valves on the gage set can be opened slowly to release the charge of refrigerant through the center hose. The gas should be released slowly so as not to pull out the oil which is throughout the system and is mixed with refrigerant.

If a puddle of oil appears at the discharge (center) hose, the flow of discharging gas should be reduced. When all gas is removed, both pressure gages will read zero. At this time, the removal and subsequent repair or replacement operations can be performed.

Evacuating. After the system has been assembled, the next step is to remove air and moisture which entered the system while it was being repaired. The removal of air and moisture from the system is called *evacuating.* A vacuum pump is used to reduce the pressure in the system and to pump out air. The vacuum pump is attached to the center hose of the gage set. The valves are both fully opened. The vacuum pump is turned on, and the system should be pumped down for at least twenty minutes. *Four hours is not too long.* The longer the evacuation time the better the removal of moisture and air. Twenty to thirty minutes is a minimum pump-down time. See Fig. 4-18.

EVACUATING (VACUUMING) THE SYSTEM

1. Gage set installed to proper service valves
2. Open gage set valves fully (counterclockwise)
3. Attach center hose to vacuum pump
4. Switch vacuum pump on
5. Low-pressure gage should begin to register a vacuum (High-side gage will attempt to register a vacuum reading but cannot)
6. When a vacuum of 26-28″ Hg occurs, continue for at *least* twenty minutes
7. If vacuum will not go to 26″ Hg, recheck all connections.
8. If vacuum reading is not satisfactory, turn gage valves both closed. If vacuum decreases (toward zero) system has a leak; stop pump-down, locate and repair the leak
9. If vacuum reading is maintained with valves closed, check vacuum pump
10. After pump-down time has elapsed, close both gage valves
11. Turn off the vacuum pump
12. System is now evacuated and ready to be charged

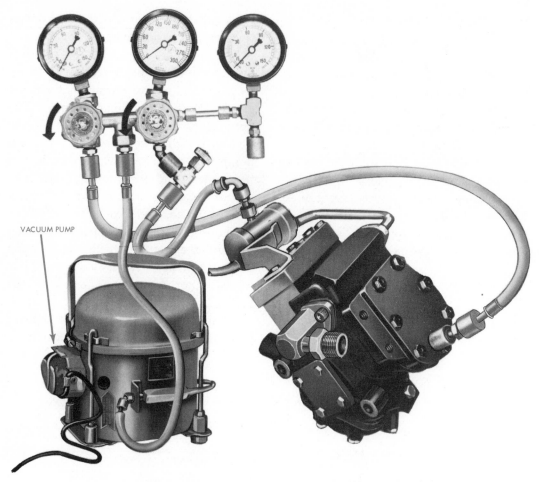

VACUUM PUMP

Fig. 4-18. Evacuating a system. (Plymouth Div., Chrysler Corp.)

Moisture Removal. As the system is being evacuated, the low-side gage on the test set will indicate a pressure below zero. The gage is indicating a vacuum, which is simply a pressure less than atmospheric pressure.

Obviously the vacuum indicates that air is being removed from the system. Most important is that moisture is also being removed. Reference was made earlier to the effect of pressure on the boiling point of liquids.

When a liquid, such as water, is under a reduced pressure, the boiling point is lowered. Now since air holds moisture, by placing the air conditioning system under a vacuum, the air can be pumped out and the moisture is caused to boil or vaporize.

Table 4-3 shows how vacuum affects the boiling point of water. Notice that as the vacuum nears thirty inches of mercury (30″ Hg), water will boil at 0°F. Obviously, the evacuation process will thor-

TABLE 4-3 BOILING POINT OF WATER
UNDER A VACUUM

SYSTEM VACUUM INCHES MERCURY	TEMPERATURE ° F BOILING POINT
24.04	140
25.39	130
26.45	120
27.32	110
27.99	100
28.50	90
28.89	80
29.18	70
29.40	60
29.66	50
29.71	40
29.76	30
29.82	20
29.86	10
29.87	5
29.88	0
29.90	-10
29.91	-20

level. At higher elevations the system will not pump down as much.

A leak check can also be made during evacuation. By closing both gage valves, the vacuum being produced by the pump is cut off from the system. Note the vacuum reading on the low-side gage at this time. After five minutes, recheck the low-side vacuum to see if it has increased. If it has increased more than one inch, there is a leak somewhere. To locate the leak, a test charge is necessary as mentioned earlier. If the vacuum reading held steady, open both high and low-side gage valves again and continue the pump-down.

When the system has been properly evacuated, it is ready to be fully recharged and given a final performance check and leak test.

To stop the evacuation, turn both valves of the gage set to the closed position. Shut off the vacuum pump and disconnect the center hose that was attached to the vacuum pump.

While this is not the place in Testing Procedures to add to the complexity of performance testing, before we turn to Charging Procedures, it is best to remind ourselves of a number of miscellaneous *Do's* and *Don't's*.

oughly dry out the system if allowed to operate for an adequate length of time. If the vacuum pump is strong and can pull down to 29 inches of vacuum, the system will be properly evacuated quickly. For lower vacuums, the pump-down will take much more time. A minimum of 28 inches vacuum is needed to insure adequate moisture removal at sea

SERVICE REMINDERS

1. Do *not* loosen fittings or clamps while the system is under pressure
2. Do *not* try to check the oil level in the compressor while the system is under pressure
3. Do *not* replace the expansion valve

without replacing the filter screen also
4. Do *not* leave open fittings and hoses exposed. Cap them so as to eliminate contamination
5. Do *not* over-charge the air condition-

ing system. This could damage the compressor reed valves

6. Do *not* service the air-conditioning system without using manifold gages and hoses
7. Do *not* use a Halide-type, propane leak-detector *inside* the car unless the doors are open
8. Do *not* assemble fittings, hoses, shaft seals and suction throttle valve dia-

phragm without spraying first with refrigerant oil

9. Do *not* try to replace shaft seal or clutch assembly without using the proper air-conditioning tools
10. Do *not* remove caps, seals or plugs from new replacement parts, until ready to install
11. Do *not* store R-12 (Freon) where temperature is above 125°F

Charging the System

The system is charged by connecting the center hose to a source of R-12, Fig. 4-19. Usually this can be a fifteen ounce disposable one-pound can or a twenty-five pound bulk dispensing tank. Fig. 4-20 illustrates a typical dispensing valve for the one-pound cans.

All air conditioners are charged by the weight of refrigerant needed. Two to four pounds of R-12 is the usual range of charge weight in automotive units. See Figs. 4-21, 4-22 and 4-23. The refrigerant can be added to the system as a vapor, or it may be introduced as a liquid.

Charging by Vapor. Gas charging is a little slower, but it is the most common and the safest method used. With the center hose attached to the R-12 source, the can or tank valve should be opened. Purge the center hose by loosening it at the gage and purge (bleed) the air out of the charging line. (The other lines should still be under vacuum).

With the system off, the high-side valve on the gage set should be opened carefully. Keep the high-side gage pressure from going above 50 psi to prevent

damage to the compressor from excessive pressures. This now allows R-12 under pressure to enter the high side of the system. Add R-12 until the system is

Fig. 4-19. Valves are attached to one pound refrigerant cans, singly or in multiples. (Robinair Manufacturing Corp.)

Fig. 4-20. Typical refrigerant dispensing valve. (Murray Corp.)

fully charged. Usually all the charge will not go in if the system is not operating. Turn off the high-side gage valve, and the remaining charge can be drawn in by starting the unit and running the compressor to assist in drawing the vapors through low-side pressure. Open the low-side gage valve slowly.

When first allowing refrigerant to enter the system, observe the other pressure gage also. It should begin to register pressure. If no pressure reading is indicated, the system is blocked, preventing the charge from flowing into the low side.

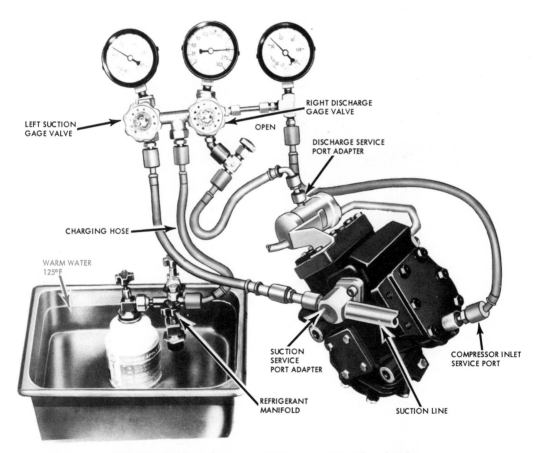

LEFT SUCTION GAGE VALVE

RIGHT DISCHARGE GAGE VALVE

OPEN

DISCHARGE SERVICE PORT ADAPTER

CHARGING HOSE

WARM WATER 125°F

SUCTION SERVICE PORT ADAPTER

REFRIGERANT MANIFOLD

SUCTION LINE

COMPRESSOR INLET SERVICE PORT

Fig. 4-21. Refrigerant can attached in normal charging situation.

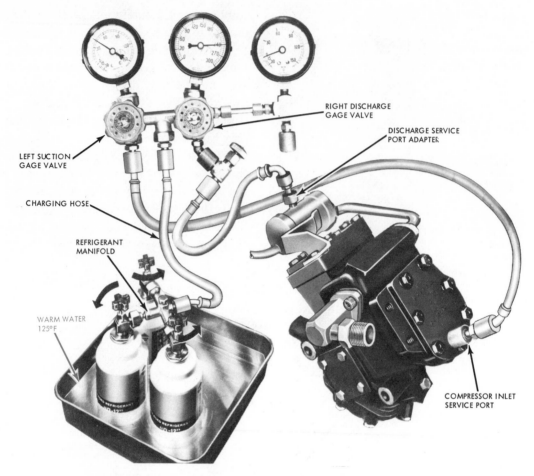

RIGHT DISCHARGE
GAGE VALVE

DISCHARGE SERVICE
PORT ADAPTER

LEFT SUCTION
GAGE VALVE

CHARGING HOSE

REFRIGERANT
MANIFOLD

WARM WATER
125°F

COMPRESSOR INLET
SERVICE PORT

Fig. 4-22. Charging a system using a multiple dispenser. (Plymouth Div., Chrysler Corp.)

CAUTION: AT NO TIME DURING CHARGING WHEN THE COMPRESSOR IS OPERATING SHOULD THE HIGH-SIDE GAGE VALVE BE OPENED. To do so would allow system high pressure to be applied to the refrigerant container. This would stop the charging and could explode the container.

If the refrigerant is slow in leaving the container because it is cold, a good procedure is to place the container in a pan of WARM, not hot, water. The warm water will raise the pressure enough so as to force the R-12 out and into the system. See Fig. 4-23.

CAUTION: Never use a flame to heat a refrigerant container.

When the proper amount of charge has been installed, check the pressure and the sight glass for bubbles. If there are bubbles, add more refrigerant until the sight glass clears.

Fig. 4-23. Refrigerant can attached to charging hose.

Fig. 4-24. With refrigerant can inverted, liquid can be admitted to the system.

When the sight glass is clear, the charge is complete. Close the low-side gage valve and disconnect the refrigerant source from the charging hose. Then remove the gage set from the service valves. Replace the covers over the valves, and the job is completed.

A leak test might be desirable to verify any repairs.

Liquid Charging. To charge, using liquid R-12, a slightly different procedure is used. The connections are made as usual to service valves and to the refrigerant source. The main difference is that, to dispense *liquid*, the refrigerant container must be turned upside down. This places liquid at the dispensing end, rather than vapor. See Fig. 4-24.

With the system OFF and under a vacuum, liquid is allowed to flow into the *high* side by opening the high-side gage valve. The liquid will flow in rapidly.

When the flow has stopped or the charge is completed, turn off the high-side valve and start up the system.

With the system operating, liquid can be slowly admitted to the *low* side of the system. Care should be used because a small amount of liquid might damage the compressor if it is allowed to flow in too rapidly. As the liquid travels through the hose from the container and the low-side hose, it is partially vaporized as it enters the system's low side.

Keep the low-side pressure below 50 psi by adjusting the low-side gage valve. Often it is just as easy to turn the R-12 can upright and complete the charging with vapor. Less chance of compressor problems will be likely. When fully charged, the sight glass will be clear and the charge complete.

It is possible to add up to a half pound more refrigerant after the sight glass clears. This normally will not over-charge the unit. Check for overcharge by disconnecting the clutch wire with the system operating. If a slug of bubbles appears within one minute, the unit is properly charged. If a longer time elapses, the system is overcharged. Release R-12 out of the center hose, and re-check for overcharge again.

When hot summer conditions exist, an occasional bubble may appear at the sight glass. This is normal and due to high temperatures.

When charging and testing, a large portable fan is sometimes necessary to provide better condensing action. This will also keep high-side pressures from rising to unsafe levels (250 psi or more).

Disconnect the R-12 source from the manifold and disconnect the manifold from the service valves. Replace valve caps and stem covers. Special note: During the previous steps, no special deviations are necessary unless a G.M. vehicle with a superheat switch is being used. Since the system would be empty, or low, during charging operations, it is necessary to disconnect the thermal limiter and connect the battery to the compressor with a jumper wire. This will allow the compressor to run and not burn out the thermal limiter. When the charging is completed, reconnect the limiter and remove the jumper wire. See Fig. 4-25. On Chrysler cars, the low-pressure switch can be simply jumped for charging.

CAUTION: When charging or using the gage set NEVER open the high-side gage valve when the system is running.

CHARGING THE SYSTEM

1. Gage set attached to service valves
2. Gage valves closed
3. System should be under a vacuum
4. Attach center gage hose to refrigerant supply
5. Open valve on R-12 container
6. Purge air from center hose by loosening hose at gage end
7. With system off, open the high-pressure gage valve. Refrigerant can be added as a vapor or liquid at this time
8. As gage pressures both reach 60-80 psi no further charging will occur
9. Close high-pressure gage valve
10. Place R-12 supply upright so as to allow vapor to enter system (See Note #1)
11. Operate engine at 1500 rpm and turn on the air conditioner at maximum cooling and highest blower speed (See Note #2)
12. Open the low-side gage valve which will admit R-12 into the system
13. Charge until proper weight of refrigerant has been added and sight glass clears. Close low-pressure gage valve. It may be necessary to place the refrigerant supply into a container of warm (150°F) water to help the flow of gas from the container (R-12)

CAUTION: *Do not apply any other form of heat to the refrigerant container.*

14. Charge is complete and vehicle should be returned to idle speed and turned OFF
15. Remove gage set carefully
16. Install protective caps on valves
17. As final check use the leak detector and check for leaks

Note #1: Liquid can be admitted on the low side with system running if the low-side pressure is not allowed to go beyond 40 psi. Liquid admission at a higher rate could damage the compressor.

Note #2: If system uses a *superheat switch,* bypass the thermal limiter with a jumper from the B to C terminals until the system is charged.

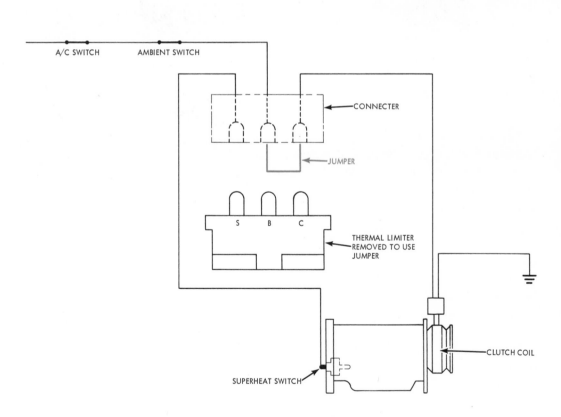

CONNECT JUMPER WIRE FROM BATTERY TO COMPRESSOR CLUTCH WIRE
WITH LIMITER WIRING PLUG REMOVED LIMITER IS NEAR COMPRESSOR

Fig. 4-25. Connect jumper wire from battery to compressor clutch wire with limiter wiring plug removed. Limiter is near blower resister. (Oldsmobile Div., General Motors Corp.)

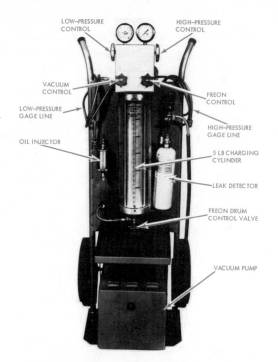

Fig. 4-26. Charging station. (Chevrolet Div., General Motors Corp.)

Fig. 4-27. This special tester is available for testing and service of air-conditioning units. (Sun Electric Corporation, Inc.)

The Charging Station. Fig. 4-26 illustrates a *charging station*. The unit is a cart on which all the gages, hoses, vacuum pump, and a supply of refrigerant are mounted. A charging cylinder is also included. The charging cylinder is a steel tank with a sight tube attached. Since the refrigerant is to be added by weight, the sight tube will indicate the liquid level in the steel tank or reservoir. The proper amount for charging a system is added to the cylinder. When the sight tube indicates the refrigerant level is zero, the system will have received its correct charge. The sight tube is graduated so it will read in pounds of R-12.

The operation of the charging cylinder will be explained by the supplier of the station.

The only other major difference in charging and evacuating is that a valve is provided to connect the vacuum pump to the gage set. Also a Freon (R-12) valve is provided to control R-12 flow into the gage set. Fig. 4-27 illustrates a type of air-conditioning testing and service unit. This unit is basically a charging

Fig. 4-28. Mobility of special tester aids servicing.

station but in addition also contains three temperature probes for ease of making temperature measurements. This unit is simple to operate and will facilitate servicing. See Fig. 4-28.

Gage Testing

Frequently a gage will become damaged, and as a result, inaccurate readings will occur. If gage damage is suspected, a simple check should be made.

Attach a can of refrigerant directly to the gage hose. Open the valve on the refrigerant container and purge the hose of air for a few seconds. Re-tighten the hose and note the pressure on the gage. It should be very close to the temperature of the refrigerant in the container.

Tape a thermometer against the refrigerant container to ascertain the temperature. If the refrigerant has been stored in a room, the temperature and pressure should reflect the temperature of the room. If it is 75°F in the room, the gage should indicate 75 pounds of pressure. If the gage does not indicate properly, turn off the refrigerant valve and disconnect the hose from the gage and the refrigerant cylinder. Inspect the hose seals and the depressor. Sometimes the seals will be damaged and block refrigerant flow, thereby causing false gage indications. Blow through the hose to be sure it is not obstructed. If in doubt, recheck the gage with a different hose. A gage which reads incorrectly must be repaired, or if repair is not possible, it should be replaced.

Keep the charging lines capped and clean to avoid damage from moisture and dirt which can enter open lines especially in the automotive service area.

Diagnosis of Pressure Abnormalities

Normal or near normal pressures, with no complaints by the owner or operator of the vehicle about poor cooling, indicate all is well.

When there are complaints the pressures will not always be normal (for many reasons). Several examples of the more common abnormal pressures and their causes are presented here.

To keep the diagnosis simple, pressures on the high side and low side are categorized as normal, high or low. Table 4-4 will give information as to the probable source of trouble. Keep in mind that ambient temperatures influence pressures. High ambient temperature will cause higher pressures, especially on the high side. Normal low-side pressure is 15 to 35 pounds. Normal high-side pressure is 175 to 240 pounds.

Checking pressure regulator valves involves more detail than checking gage pressures. The procedure is determined by the type of valve used. The POA valve used by General Motors and some

Ford vehicles is quite simple to check. The check of the EPR valve used by Chrysler is more difficult. All checks are made with the gage manifold set attached and the system operating as for the performance test.

POA Valve

The check of POA valve operation involves merely measuring the low-side pressure, which is picked up at the POA valve itself. The correct reading is 28.5 psi at sea level. Since different altitudes will cause a change in that pressure, a chart is provided which gives elevations and proper pressure readings. If the pressure readings are not as specified, the

TABLE 4-4 ABNORMAL PRESSURE CHART

PRESSURE CHARACTERISTIC	PROBABLE CAUSE
1 Low side is low High side is normal	1 Expansion valve plugged or stuck closed 2 Thermostat defective 3 Moisture in system
2 Low side is high High side is normal	1 Expansion valve stuck in open position 2 Capillary sensing bulb loose or uninsulated 3 Check sight glass for low charge
3 Low side is high High side is low	1 Compressor defective
4 High side is high Low side is normal	1 Too much refrigerant in system 2 Air in system 3 Air flow restrictions at condenser 4 Restriction in condenser, drier or high side line 5 Overheating engine
5 Low side is low High side is low	1 Low charge

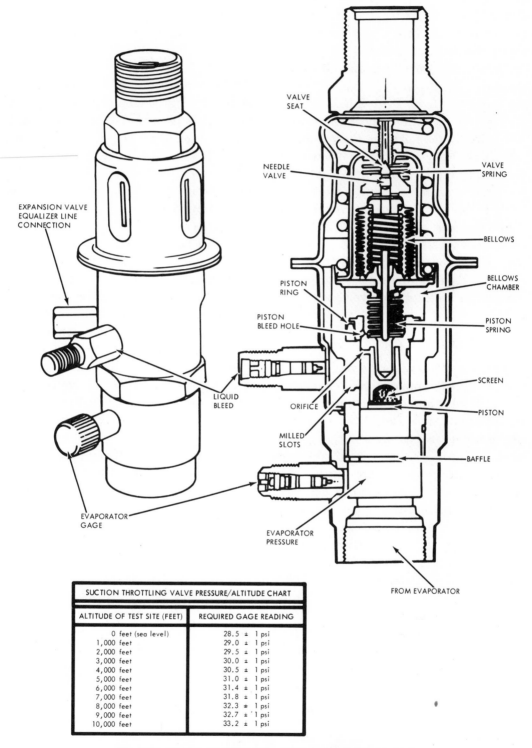

VALVE
SEAT

NEEDLE
VALVE

EXPANSION VALVE
EQUALIZER LINE
CONNECTION

VALVE
SPRING

BELLOWS

PISTON
RING

BELLOWS
CHAMBER

PISTON
BLEED HOLE

PISTON
SPRING

LIQUID
BLEED

ORIFICE

SCREEN

PISTON

MILLED
SLOTS

BAFFLE

EVAPORATOR
GAGE

EVAPORATOR
PRESSURE

FROM EVAPORATOR

SUCTION THROTTLING VALVE PRESSURE/ALTITUDE CHART	
ALTITUDE OF TEST SITE (FEET)	REQUIRED GAGE READING
0 feet (sea level)	28.5 ± 1 psi
1,000 feet	29.0 ± 1 psi
2,000 feet	29.5 ± 1 psi
3,000 feet	30.0 ± 1 psi
4,000 feet	30.5 ± 1 psi
5,000 feet	31.0 ± 1 psi
6,000 feet	31.4 ± 1 psi
7,000 feet	31.8 ± 1 psi
8,000 feet	32.3 ± 1 psi
9,000 feet	32.7 ± 1 psi
10,000 feet	33.2 ± 1 psi

Fig. 4-29. Suction throttling valve and pressure/altitude chart.

POA valve must be replaced. Note that as elevations increase, the pressure also increases slightly. See Fig. 4-29.

With a POA valve, it is difficult to determine if the expansion valve is operating properly. If the POA valve readings are higher than normal, check the expansion valve by the following procedure.

Operate the system with the blower on *low*. Remove the expansion valve bulb from the evaporator tailpipe. Note the low-side pressure. Place the expansion valve bulb in a glass of ice. This should cause POA pressure to drop to 30 psi. If there is no pressure drop, the POA valve is defective. If the pressure is much less than 30 psi the expansion valve is defective.

EPR Valve Check

With manifold gages installed (*third gage required*), proceed as follows to check the EPR and expansion valve. The air conditioner must be tested at 75°F, engine idling and controls set at *maximum A/C* or *recirculate*, with the blower on high speed. High-side pressure should be between 140 to 210 pounds. At this time note the low-side gage readings. The readings should be within 4 pounds of each other. If not, the EPR valve is defective. See Fig. 4-30.

To check the expansion valve, the bulb must be removed from its well at the evaporator tailpipe. See Fig. 4-31. Hold the bulb in your hand to warm it up for several minutes. The warm bulb should open the expansion valve, resulting in a pressure of at least 40 psi on the low-side gages. •

Next, the expansion valve bulb should be immersed in 5 inches of ice and water at 32°F. Low-side pressure should drop

to 21 to 25 psi. If not, speed up the engine and observe the low-side pressure. If it does drop to 21 to 25 psi the compressor is faulty.

With the expansion valve bulb in ice water (32°F), the suction pressure should be 21 to 25 psi and the compressor inlet pressure should be 17 psi or less; if not, the EPR valve is to be replaced.

If system pressures are all normal, the refrigeration system can be eliminated as a source of trouble.

Improper operation of the controls by the driver frequently can be the cause of cooling problems. Expecting too much from an air conditioner is also a typical problem. A vehicle which is parked in the hot sun will be soaked with heat. This heat is not easily nor quickly removed. If the windows are opened, and the vehicle driven with the air conditioner on for several minutes, the hot air will be expelled more rapidly. Windows can then be closed and the A/C system should function as designed.

On-and-off type of operation in very hot weather is a difficult circumstance to overcome. The A/C unit works better if it is in continuous operation with the vehicle moving.

Keep in mind that the electrical components and the vacuum operated controls must all be performing properly if adequate cooling is to be achieved.

Vacuum Checks

Vacuum operation can be checked readily with a vacuum gage. Install the vacuum gage in the main supply line to the air conditioner control unit. Usually this will be near the rear of the engine or on the fire wall. This, however, is not to be pure intake manifold vacuum. When

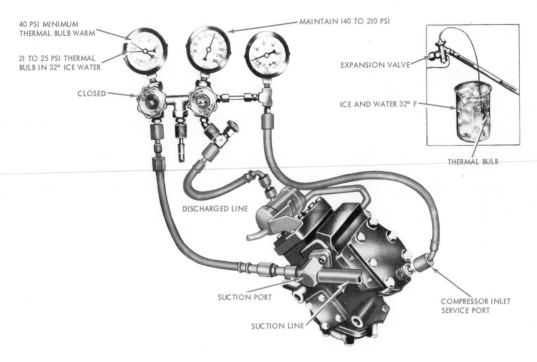

Fig. 4-30. Expansion valve and EPR test valve. (Plymouth Div., Chrysler Corp.)

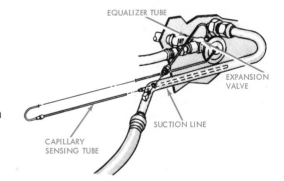

Fig. 4-31. Capillary sensing tube removed from well. (Plymouth Div., Chrysler Corp.)

the gage is installed in the A/C system, the engine can be started up and a vacuum reading should be observed on the gage. When the reading is above 16 inches, the engine can be turned off. The reading should not drop if all the controls are in OFF position. If the vacuum reading drops, the reservoir tank, lines and check valve should be closely inspected as they may be leaking. A good system will hold a steady vacuum reading with the engine shut off.

With the gage holding a steady reading, the vacuum operated components can be checked from the driver's seat.

Move the control lever to the first position away from OFF. If a vacuum operated component is activated, a drop of

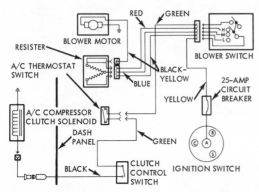

Fig. 4-32. **Typical compressor clutch and blower circuit. (Ford Motor Co.)**

Fig. 4-33. **An ohmmeter or self-powered test light along with salt and ice water will force the thermostatic switch to open its contacts.**

not more than 1 inch of vacuum is expected. A total loss of vacuum pinpoints a leak in that component or its supply hose.

Operate the control lever through all positions noting vacuum drop at each point.

A vacuum operated water valve can also be checked by moving the temperature lever from *maximum cool* to *maximum hot*. Again a small vacuum drop indicates the vacuum operation is good.

If this method does not locate the vacuum problem, a vacuum pump can be used along with a probe fabricated from spare tubing and hoses. Connect a vacuum gage at the vacuum pump, and use a bleed valve to control the vacuum to exactly 8 inches. When 8 inches of vacuum can be repeatedly seen on the gage by covering and uncovering the probe, the set-up is ready for use. Place the probe into the vacuum lines at the main supply line to the air-conditioning unit. Repeat the vacuum drop test cycle as indicated in the preceding paragraph. After

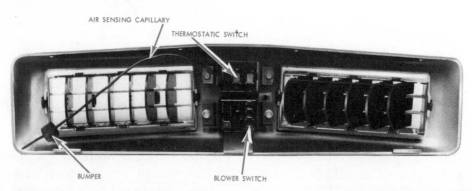

Fig. 4-34. **Location of blower and thermostat switches on a hang-on type unit. (Chevrolet Div., General Motors Corp.)**

each drop, the gage should return to the 8 inch setting. This is because the vacuum pump is continuously supplying vacuum.

The test probe can be used at the connector plug located at the rear of the main control on the dash panel to localize suspected vacuum motors or lines.

Most vacuum problems are a result of pinched or poorly routed lines. Occasionally a line has been pulled off by accident. Always make a visual check to determine that all hoses are connected properly. Most vacuum units are located inside the vehicle and are reasonably safe from weather and other disturbances. Removal of a dash panel or glove box liner often will provide access to the major units.

Electrical components are most easily checked by using a test light to determine that electricity is able to pass through the switch as it is operated. See Figs. 4-32, 4-33 and 4-34. If this is not convenient, it is also possible to use a jumper wire to by-pass a switch as a test.

Many electrical problems, as with vacuum problems, can be located with a careful visual inspection. Slip-on connectors are often sources of poor contact. Sometimes just pulling the connector apart and after examination, reconnecting, will correct problems.

Fig. 4-35 illustrates two thermometers which are available for temperature checking. The dial type has a metal cover on its length. This prevents accidental breakage, which occurs easily with the glass type.

Tools such as these thermometers and the gage set are most valuable to proper air-conditioning testing. Keep all test equipment clean and safely stored so it will be ready for use.

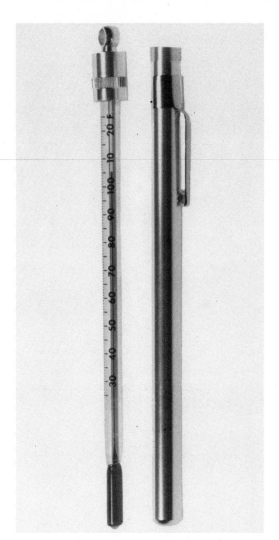

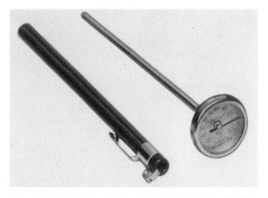

Fig. 4-35. Typical A/C test thermometers. (Robinair Manufacturing Corp.)

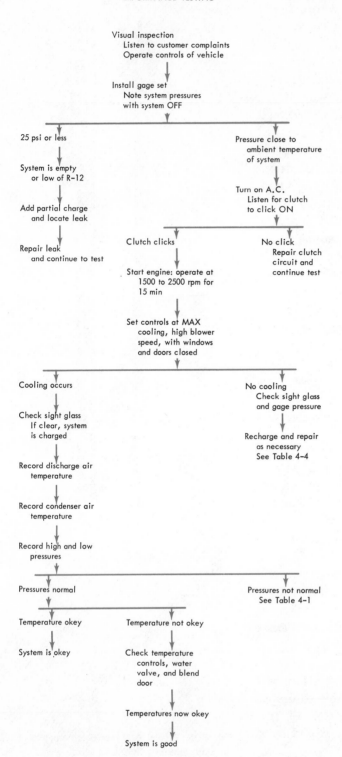

Fig. 4-36.

AIR CONDITIONING DIAGNOSIS GUIDE

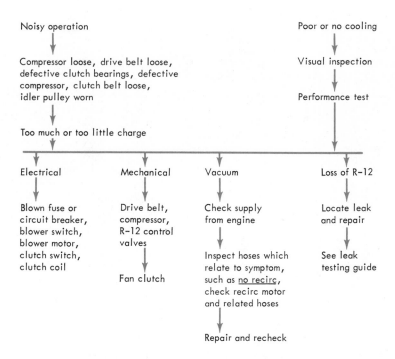

Fig. 4-37.

Trouble Shooting Procedures

As system service is an important operation, several guides have been prepared to assist in developing the skill and confidence needed for servicing an air conditioned vehicle. See Figs. 4-36 and 4-37.

Although there are a great number of problems that can develop with the A/C unit the most frequently heard complaint is that of insufficient or poor cooling. A thorough visual inspection and a routine performance test will usually pinpoint the source of trouble rapidly.

The service and diagnosis guides which follow are designed to assist in performing basic trouble-shooting and service operations on the air conditioned vehicle.

It is recognized that not every defect which could be encountered is mentioned in the diagnosis guides. Such a detailed listing usually is too complex to follow. The guide lists the most common types of problems which will be encountered.

The service guides are designed to provide a simple step by step procedure to

PRESSURE DIAGNOSIS GUIDE
(NON–CYCLING SYSTEMS)

LOW PRESSURE At Compressor	LOW PRESSURE At Evaporator		HIGH PRESSURE	PROBLEM
4–26 psi	G.M. POA Chrysler	28–32 psi 21–25 psi	175–230 psi	Normal
1. Normal	Too high or too low		Normal	Evaporator pressure valve, EPR or POA defective, moisture in unit possible cause
2. Normal	Normal		Too high	Poor air flow over condenser, restriction in system high side, look for cool spot or frost ring, engine over-heating, air in system, fluid drive fan is inoperative
3. Too high	Normal or too high		Too high	Poor air flow over condenser, over-charged unit
4. Too high	Normal or high		Too low	Compressor failure
5. Too low	Normal or too low		Too low	Overcharged unit, TXV stuck closed
6. Too high	Normal or high		Normal or too high	TXV capillary sensing bulb poorly attached or insulated, TXV stuck open

Fig. 4-38.

follow when performing such operations as inspection, pressure testing, discharging, evacuating, charging, and leak testing of the air conditioner.

Finally, several charts are provided to assist in interpreting system pressures. See Figs. 4-38, 4-39 and 4-40. A chart for the cycling system and the non-cycling system is included. A separate chart deals with interpreting pressures on systems which use the valves in receiver control assembly (VIR).

Problems to Consider

1. Attach a gage set to a system which uses manual service valves. Purge lines, then operate the system and record the pressures. Remove the gage set.

2. Attach a gage set to a system equipped with Schrader type valves. Purge lines, then operate the system and record the pressures. Remove the gage set.

PRESSURE DIAGNOSIS GUIDE
(CYCLING SYSTEMS)

LOW PRESSURE	HIGH PRESSURE	PROBLEM
1. 5–36 psi	175–230 psi	Normal
2. Normal	Too high	Poor air flow over condenser, restriction in lines, look for cool spot or frost ring, engine overheating, air in system, fluid drive fan inoperative, over-charged system
3. Too high	Too high	Poor air flow over condenser, overcharged system
4. Too high	Too low	Compressor failure
5. Too low	Too low	Undercharged unit
6. Goes into vacuum	Normal	TXV stuck closed, ice at TXV due to moisture in system
7. Too high	Normal or above	Capillary sensing bulb poorly attached or insulated
8. Normal, but cooling erratic	Normal	Moisture in system

Fig. 4-39.

DIAGNOSIS GUIDE FOR VIR SYSTEMS
(NON-CYCLING)

LOW PRESSURE	HIGH PRESSURE	PROBLEM
1. 28–32 psi	175–230 psi	Normal
2. Normal or too low	Too low	Undercharged, check sight glass for bubbles, liquid pick-up tube partially plugged, could cause superheat switch to blow thermal limiter
3. Very low	Very high	No charge in unit
4. Normal	Too high	Overcharged
5. Too low	Too low	Replace expansion valve capsule
6. Too high	Too low	Replace POA valve capsule
7. Normal or low	Too low	Erratic cooling, evaporator may ice up, replace POA valve capsule
8. Too high	Normal	Replace POA valve capsule

Fig. 4-40.

3. With a gage set attached, discharge the refrigerant from an air-conditioning system.

4. Attach a vacuum pump to a discharged system and pump down for at least 30 minutes. How can you detect a leak?

5. Recharge an evacuated system using refrigerant as a liquid. Complete the charge with vapor.

6. Describe how you can determine if a system is properly charged. How can you determine if the system was overcharged?

7. Using a leak detector check a complete system for leaks.

8. With a gage set attached and a system operating, place restrictions in front of the condenser for a few minutes. What happens? Why?

9. With a gage set attached and a system operating, note the high-side reading. Place a large fan so greater air flow is produced at the condenser. What happens? Why?

10. Make a performance test of a fully charged hang-on type A/C system. Record your observations.

11. Make a performance test of a fully charged factory installed A/C system. Report your results and recommendations.

12. Check the gages for accuracy as described in Gage Testing. What are your results?

13. On a Chrysler system which requires use of a third gage, check that the EPR valve is functioning. Use a shop manual for exact specifications. What are your results and recommendations?

14. Check a G.M. system which has a POA valve. How can a defective POA valve be identified? What are your results?

15. Attach a vacuum gage with a tee into the vacuum supply system of a factory A/C system. With a gage reading of at least 16 inches of vacuum stop the engine. Does the vacuum hold? Operate vacuum controls slowly, noticing whether a slight vacuum drop occurs as the vacuum units operate. Does a water control valve operate also? List the steps taken and your results and recommendations.

16. Locate the evaporator drain tubes or provisions on several different vehicles. Could any of these drains become plugged? Describe what you observed during this problem.

17. If you have access to a charging station or charging cylinder, use it to discharge, evacuate and recharge a system.

18. Install an air conditioner in a vehicle. Describe what major steps were involved.

Trade Competency Check

1. What are the two types of service valves used on air-conditioning units?

2. Describe a typical air conditioning gage set.

3. What is the normal position for a manual type service valve?

4. When would a service valve be front-seated?

5. How is the Schrader type service valve cracked open?

6. Describe how to remove a charging hose from a Schrader type valve.

7. What is the purpose of the valves on the manifold gage set?

8. What is the purpose of the center hose on a manifold gage set?

9. Why might a needle valve be necessary on the high-pressure line?

10. When is a third or extra low-side gage necessary?

11. Describe how to purge the hoses of the gage set.

12. What is meant by the term *performance test*?

13. What is considered to be normal low-side and high-side pressure?

14. What effect will higher ambient temperatures have on pressures?

15. What is indicated when a sight glass is clear?

16. How can you determine that a system is not overcharged?

17. How much pressure should there be before leak testing is attempted?

18. How does a flame-type leak detector indicate a leak?

19. When discharging a system, what is indicated if a puddle of oil appears at the discharge hose end?

20. What position are the manifold gage valves

Leak Testing Procedures and Trouble Shooting

in when discharging? Evacuating?

21. What is the minimum pump-down time?
22. If a system will not hold a vacuum for five minutes what is indicated?
23. Evacuation is the process of removing what two undesirable substances from an air conditioner?
24. How is R-12 dispensed into a system?
25. Describe how to charge a system with vapor.
26. Describe how to charge a system with liquid.
27. Why is a pan of warm water helpful when charging a system?
28. When a system is operating, when would be a good time to open the high-side manifold gage?
29. How could you determine that a gage was operating properly?
30. If the ambient temperature is 90°F, the low-side pressure is 45 psi and the high-side pressure is 210 psi, what is the condition of the system? Will there be adequate cooling?
31. When a POA valve is used how can you determine whether the expansion valve is faulty?
32. When an EPR valve is suspected of being defective, what is the procedure to follow?

5 Compressor Trouble Shooting and Service

This chapter discusses the various types of service which can be performed on air conditioning components, especially the compressor and its clutch. (The clutch is the only moving part of the system, aside from sensing systems, switches and blower motors.)

The compressor service problems presented are typical, and the steps of diagnosis and service are explained in detail. It is necessary to recognize that identification of defective components and the use of the correct method of servicing them is of the greatest importance.

Compressor clutches and their gas seals are among the most common problems. However, when an item is in need of service or repair, the information in this chapter should be comprehensive enough to lead to solutions for most of the problems which do occur, aside from the leakage problems treated in Chapter 3.

Service to any gas containing component requires that the R-12 pressure be released by discharging the system as described in Chapter 4.

The compressor clutch, drive belt, vacuum, and electrical devices can all be serviced without discharging the refrigerant.

When a system has been discharged and components are serviced, care should be taken to keep all tools and parts clean and dry. Cap or plug all disconnected lines. Leave lines covered until the actual installation.

Compressor Clutch Trouble Shooting and Service

The compressor clutch can fail to operate, slip at higher compressor speeds, or be noisy. Slipping will be evidenced by unusual wear on the clutch surfaces, and usually a screeching sound will be heard at higher speeds. See Fig. 5-1.

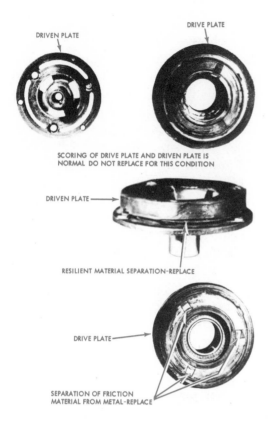

DRIVEN PLATE

DRIVE PLATE

SCORING OF DRIVE PLATE AND DRIVEN PLATE IS
NORMAL DO NOT REPLACE FOR THIS CONDITION

DRIVEN PLATE

RESILIENT MATERIAL SEPARATION-REPLACE

DRIVE PLATE

SEPARATION OF FRICTION
MATERIAL FROM METAL-REPLACE

Fig. 5-1. Compressor clutch wear. (Ford Motor Co.)

The electrical test for all compressor clutches requires connecting an ammeter to the clutch coil wire and the car battery. If the current draw is not within specifications, usually two to three amperes (four to five for aluminum coils), the coil is defective. Clutch coils are generally of the stationary field coil type and will have to be replaced if electrically not within specifications.

A clutch coil which uses a rotating magnetic field coil, however, will use brushes. These should be checked to see that they are making clean contact with the metal slip ring on the coil.

A noisy clutch is often a cause of complaint. Because noises can telegraph from

the compressor area, check carefully to be certain the clutch is the source of noise. Often a loose drive belt can produce a noise called *belt rumble* which can be mistaken for clutch or compressor noise. A loose compressor or a noisy compressor can also cause incorrect replacement of the clutch. First check the drive belt and its tension. Also check any idler pulleys which can produce noises.

When a clutch has been determined in fact to be noisy, it should be removed and replaced with a new or rebuilt unit. If only a bearing is producing the noise, a replacement bearing can be installed. See Fig. 5-2.

Clutch Service

To replace a clutch involves the use of special tools. Normally the clutch can be serviced with the compressor intact. The clutch pulley is removed after the belt and pulley bolt have been removed. It is good practice to remove the pulley bolt before disconnecting the clutch lead or drive belt. This will help prevent the clutch and shaft from turning when loosening the bolt. A spanner wrench is also helpful to hold the shaft from rotating.

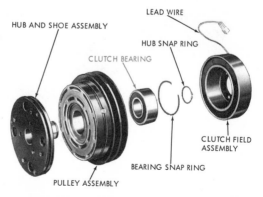

LEAD WIRE

HUB AND SHOE ASSEMBLY

HUB SNAP RING

CLUTCH BEARING

CLUTCH FIELD
ASSEMBLY

BEARING SNAP RING

PULLEY ASSEMBLY

Fig. 5-2. Warner clutch. (Plymouth Div., Chrysler Corp.)

Fig. 5-3. Removing compressor clutch. (Ford Motor Co.)

PULLER C-3787

Fig. 5-4. Removal of hub and shoe assembly and bearings requires special tools—Warner clutch. (Plymouth Div., Chrysler Corp.)

When the bolt is removed, a $5/8$-11 × $2\frac{1}{2}$ inch cap screw in most cases can be threaded into the pulley hub. See Fig. 5-3. This large bolt acts as a puller and will easily remove the pulley. Do not pry or use a hammer or you may cause further damage to the compressor. With the pulley removed, remove the clutch unit and unscrew the field coil assembly from the front of the compressor. Then remove the coil.

Special tools are needed to disassemble the clutch pulley, hub and bearings. Consult a shop manual for the proper tools if disassembly is necessary. See Fig. 5-4.

This clutch procedure will service all but the Frigidaire compressor used on General Motors cars and some Ford products. See Fig. 5-5. Clutch removal of Frigidaire compressors requires special tools. The tool supplier includes directions on how to properly remove the G. M. clutch and pulley. Clutch removal is in three steps: (1) The first is removal of the drive hub. See Fig. 5-6. (2) The

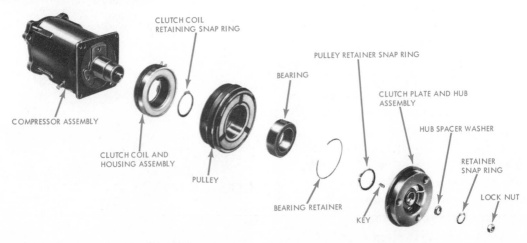

CLUTCH COIL RETAINING SNAP RING

PULLEY RETAINER SNAP RING

BEARING

CLUTCH PLATE AND HUB ASSEMBLY

COMPRESSOR ASSEMBLY

HUB SPACER WASHER

CLUTCH COIL AND HOUSING ASSEMBLY

RETAINER SNAP RING

PULLEY

LOCK NUT

BEARING RETAINER

KEY

Fig. 5-5. Six-cylinder compressor clutch. (Ford Motor Co.)

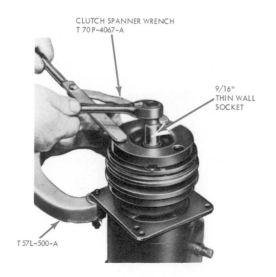

CLUTCH SPANNER WRENCH
T 70 P-4067-A

9/16"
THIN WALL
SOCKET

T 57L-500-A

REMOVING LOCK NUT

HUB DRIVEN
PLATE REMOVER
T71P-19703-E

CLUTCH DRIVEN PLATE

CLUTCH ASSEMBLY

REMOVING DRIVEN PLATE

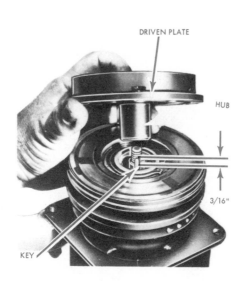

DRIVEN PLATE

HUB

3/16"

KEY

ALIGNING DRIVEN PLATE KEY

BEARING RETAINER RING

BEARING

PULLEY RETAINING
RING

DRIVE PLATE

LOCATION OF BEARINGS AND
PULLEY RETAINERS

Fig. 5-6. Location of bearings and pulley retainers. (Ford Motor Co.)

PULLEY REMOVER
T71P-19703-B

ABSORBENT SLEEVE
RETAINER REPLACER
T71P-19703-N

REMOVING PULLEY AND DRIVE PLATE

BEARING AND PULLEY
ASSEMBLY REPLACER
AND BEARING REMOVER
T71P-19703-D

PULLEY

REMOVING BEARING FROM PULLEY

BEARING AND PULLEY
ASSEMBLY REPLACER
AND BEARING REMOVER
T71P-19703-D

PULLEY

BEARING

INSTALLING BEARING IN PULLEY

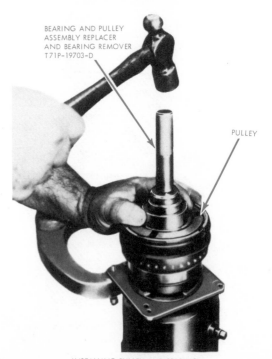

BEARING AND PULLEY
ASSEMBLY REPLACER
AND BEARING REMOVER
T71P-19703-D

PULLEY

INSTALLING PULLEY AND BEARING
ASSEMBLY ON COMPRESSOR

Fig. 5-7. Removing pulley in order to install bearing. (Ford Motor Co.)

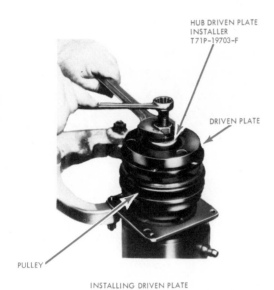

Fig. 5-9. Removing crankshaft bearing housing. (Plymouth Div., Chrysler Corp.)

Fig. 5-8. Installing driven plate. (Ford Motor Co.)

second is removal of the pulley which is pressed onto the compressor. See Fig. 5-7. (3) The third is the removal of the clutch coil by removing a snap ring. Fig. 5-8 shows the tools needed to replace the driven plate after both plates have been removed. It is necessary to maintain a clearance between the drive plate and the pulley of $\frac{1}{32}''$ to $\frac{1}{16}''$ as these are put together. Replacement is the reverse of the removal steps.

Shaft Seals

Compressor shaft seal leakage is a normal service problem. Frequently the refrigerant charge is lost because of a defective compressor shaft seal.

The clutch pulley and drive hub must be removed to service a gas seal. A seal plate is readily removed on either the York or Tecumseh compressors. The Chrysler compressor has provision for two screwdriver blades to be used to pry

off the retainer and seal seat from the compressor. See Fig. 5-9.

Compressor seals are very delicate. Be careful not to touch any part of the seal seat or seal surface with the fingers. Acid from the skin will etch the seal surface, rendering it useless. The shaft seal is usually two or more pieces, with a steel seat on which a spring-loaded carbon or ceramic seal will ride. See Fig. 5-10. An O-ring also provides a seal between the compressor seal housing and the seal itself, Fig. 5-11. The compressor shaft turns the carbon or ceramic seal as it turns. A seal is then provided between the rotating shaft and the stationary seal seat.

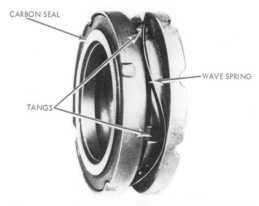

Fig. 5-10. Cartridge type gas seal. (Chrysler Corp.)

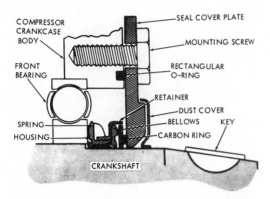

Fig. 5-11. York compressor gas seal. (Ford Motor Co.)

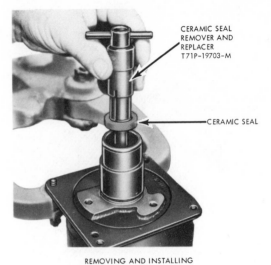

REMOVING AND INSTALLING CERAMIC SEAL SEAT

Fig. 5-13. Removing and installing ceramic seal seat. (Ford Motor Co.)

The pressure of the refrigerant and spring pressure keep the seal firmly seated. If care is not taken when installing a new seal assembly, a leak will very likely result.

G.M. Compressor Seal Removal

The G.M. compressor must be removed from the vehicle to replace the compressor seal, Fig. 5-12. The drive hub is to be

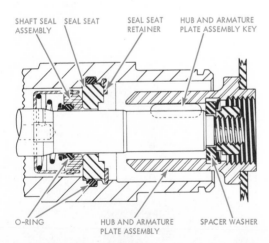

Fig. 5-12. Cross section of a compressor shaft seal area. (Oldsmobile Div., General Motors Corp.)

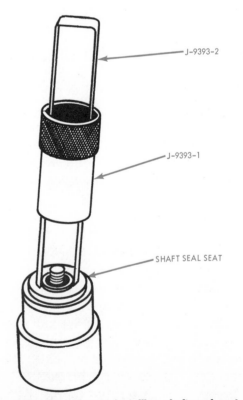

Fig. 5-14. Removing or installing shaft seal seat.

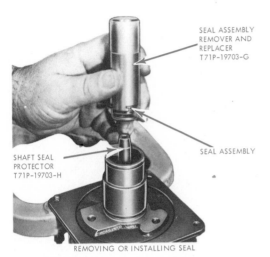

Fig. 5-15. Removing and installing seal. (Ford Motor Co.)

Fig. 5-16. Lubricate with refrigerant oil. (Plymouth Div., Chrysler Corp.)

removed before the seal is accessible (Fig. 5-6).

The removal of the seal requires snap-ring pliers; then the seal seat retainer can be removed. The seal seat is removed by the special tool shown in Figs. 5-13 and 5-14. Newer seats are ceramic, while the older design used a steel seat.

The O-ring for the seal seat needs to be removed. The last step is to remove the shaft seal assembly with the special tool as shown in Fig. 5-15. If seal removal is attempted without the special tools, damage to the compressor shaft or the new seal is very likely.

Lubricate all seals and O-rings with clean refrigerant oil. A squirt can or an aerosol can may be used. See Fig. 5-16.

Compressor Service

If diagnosis during performance testing (Chapter 4) has indicated a faulty compressor, it must be removed for service. Before a compressor is serviced, the oil level must be determined. Several factors need to be considered before service can proceed.

All of the oil in the refrigeration system does not remain in the compressor during operation. Some circulates with the R-12 constantly. This means that

checking for the presence of refrigerant oil in an air conditioner is not as simple a procedure as checking engine oil level. Most compressors have a screw which can be removed for oil checking. See Fig. 5-17. G.M. compressors have no provision for checking oil.

Regardless, the refrigerant must be discharged to check oil level unless the compressor can be isolated by front-seating both manual service valves. A dip-

Fig. 5-17. Removing compressor filler plug. (Ford Motor Co.)

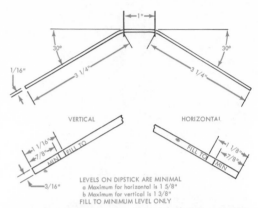

Fig. 5-19. Tecumseh compressor oil level dipstick. (Ford Motor Co.)

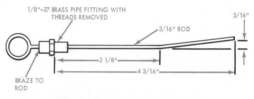

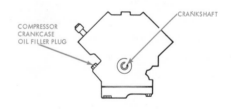

stick can then be made from a steel rod according to the type of compressor being serviced. See Figs. 5-18, 5-19, 5-20 and 5-21. (No G.M. type is shown.)

When the system has been in operation, the amount of oil in the compressor will vary, depending on speed and air conditioning load. At higher rpms, less oil will be retained in the compressor. It is important that the proper oil level be maintained in the system for proper lubrication of compressor and the expansion valve.

Fig. 5-20. V-2 type compressor dipstick. (Chrysler Corp.)

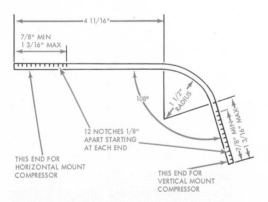

Fig. 5-18. York compressor oil level dipstick. (Ford Motor Co.)

Fig. 5-21. Compressor oil level check. (Ford Motor Co.)

Checking Oil Level

Oil level should be determined before the compressor is disassembled. Oil is constantly being circulated with the refrigerant. For this reason, oil level in the compressor is determined by draining the used oil from the compressor. This used oil should be measured and discarded.

When the compressor is ready for reinstallation, the same amount of fresh oil should be added. When installing a new or an exchange compressor, the new oil supply is to be drained and saved. Replace only the amount which was drained from the old compressor. An exception is made to this procedure when the quantity of old oil is low. In that case, the full oil quantity should be restored to the compressor. See Table 5-1.

The system, however, will not require oil addition unless an oil leak has occurred or a major component has been replaced.

Oil Addition

The approximate oil quantity that is lost when a component is replaced is: Evaporator—3 oz; Condenser—1 oz; Receiver—2 oz. The replacement oil should be poured directly into the component if possible. If not, it must be added to the compressor oil. Table 5-1 shows a procedure to follow when replacing compressor oil supply according to five major conditions. The quantities referred to are for G.M. compressors only. The same technique, however, is appropriate with compressors which hold a smaller amount of oil. With other compressors, since they can be checked with a dipstick, it is not difficult to determine the oil level.

Oil can be added to the G.M. compressor through the drain plug. However, always use refrigerant oil, never a substitute. Refrigerant oil is foam-resistant and wax-free, in addition to being chemically stable with R-12. Oil viscosity ranges from 525 to 1000 centipoise (cs). (Centipoise is the standard unit of viscosity.)

Follow the compressor manufacturer's recommendations. Oil in the refrigeration system should always be clean. If oil drained from a compressor is dark, or contains fine particles, the entire system should be flushed with R-12, or with R-11 which is made for flushing. Also, the receiver-drier should be replaced. Add sufficient oil with replacement components, as mentioned earlier.

Adding Oil to G.M. System

A special method is available which allows the addition of oil to the system without removing the compressor. This is especially helpful on G.M. compressor installations. The oil is contained in a 14 ounce can which is composed of 12 ounces of R-12 and 2 ounces of refrigerant oil or a 4 ounce can with 2 ounces of R-12 and 2 ounces of oil. When it is desired to add 2 or 4 ounces of oil, the special oil charge can is attached to the center hose of the gage set.

The refrigerant can is then inverted and the oil is allowed to slowly enter the low side by opening the low-side gage valve. This is an especially valuable time-saver in cases where only a hose or line has obviously leaked oil out of the system.

After the leak is repaired and the system evacuated, an oil charge is used to replace the oil lost from the leaking line.

TABLE 5-1

Procedure Recommended for oil level determination (G.M. 6-cylinder compressor)

CONDITION	AMOUNT OF OIL DRAINED	AMOUNT OF 525 OIL TO INSTALL	EXAMPLES
I Major loss of oil and a component has to be replaced	a More than 4 oz See Note 1 and 3 b Less than 4 oz	a Amount drained from compressor plus amount for component being replaced as follows: Custom Evaporator 3 oz Cool Pack Evaporator 2 oz Condenser 1 oz Receiver-Dehydrator 1 oz Neglect any slight oil coating lost in case of hose, line, TXV, or STV change b Install 6 oz plus amount for component being replaced as shown above	Leak in evaporator, condenser, or receiver-dehydrator, bad compressor seal leak, hose failure major fitting leak, collision damage Same as above
IIA Compressor being replaced with a service compressor	a More than 4 oz See Note 1 and 3 b Less than 4 oz	a After draining new compressor, replace same amount that was drained from replaced compressor. b Same as above except add 6 oz oil to the compressor	Extremely noisy compressor, malfunctioning compressor Same as above
IIB Compressor is replaced with a field reoperated compressor	a Same as IIA (a) See Note 1 and 3 b Same as IIA (b)	a Same as IIA except add an additional ounce of oil to compressor (More oil is retained in a drained compressor than one that has been rebuilt) b Same as above applies to IIB (7 oz)	Compressor in IIA is completely disassembled and reoperated Same as above
III Same as step IIA and B except Note 2 applies (no evidence of major leak and that little or no oil has left system)	a More than 1 1/2 oz See Note 2 and 3 b Less than 1 1/2 oz	a Same as IIA b Same as IIB	System out of Freon, compressor seized, clutch inoperative and/or damaged Same as above
IV Same as Step I, II, and III except system is contaminated	a Any amount See Note 4	a Install 10 1/2 oz to replacement or reoperated compressor	Oil jet black and and gritty, sludge or metallic particles evident, rust or free water evident

NOTE 1 Prior to compressor removal the compressor should be idled for 10 minutes at 1000-1500 engine RPM, maximum refrigeration, high blower, whenever possible

NOTE 2 (a) Do not idle the compressor as stated in Note 1 if the compressor is internally damaged, the system is out of Freon, a major leak is evident in the system, or compressor seal is badly leaking, so further harm will not be caused to the compressor (b) If the clutch circuit or coil has an electrical failure or compressor clutch is damaged, or compressor is seized it will not be possible to run the compressor prior to removal

NOTE 3 Remove compressor and place in a horizontal position with drain plug downward, drain compressor, measure quantity of oil drained and then discard it

NOTE 4 Oil drained contains foreign material such as chips, or there is evidence of moisture in the system, proceed as follows: Replace receiver-dehydrator and flush all component parts and replace damaged parts where necessary

With this oil charge R-12 is added to the system as well. Two ounces are normally adequate for one leak; it can be *assumed* that approximately two ounces were lost from the leak.

Repairs on Reciprocating Type Compressors

General compressor overhaul is not recommended. However, it is possible to disassemble a compressor and to replace various parts which are defective as shown in Figs. 5-22, 5-23 and 5-24.

The two most frequent types of compressor repairs involve the valve plate and head gasket. If the compressor requires more service than the above, it is recommended that an exchange compressor be installed. It is the more economical and quickest method of getting the air conditioner back into operation.

The cylinder head and valve plate on the majority of compressors is simply removed by unscrewing the bolts which attach the head to the compressor cylinder block. The cylinder head and valve

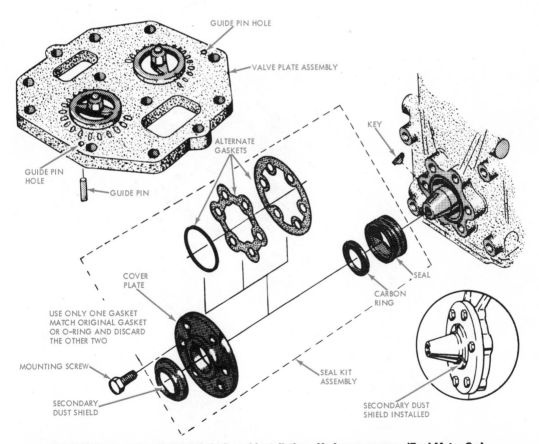

Fig. 5-22. Valve plate and crankshaft seal installation—York compressor. (Ford Motor Co.)

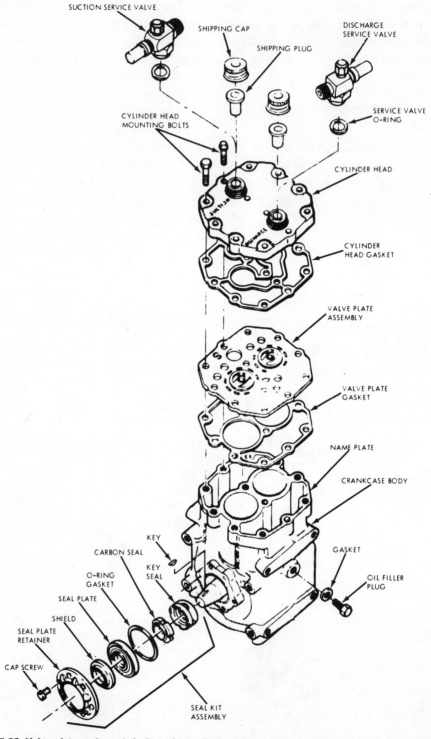

Fig. 5-23. Valve plate and crankshaft seal installation—Tecumseh compressor. (Ford Motor Co.)

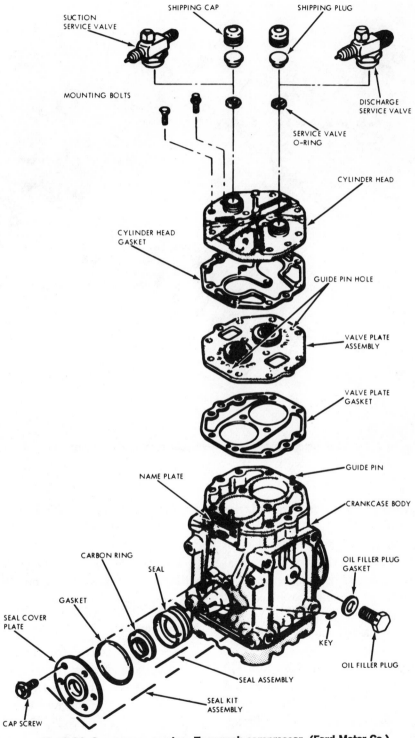

Fig. 5-24. Compressor service—Tecumseh compressor. (Ford Motor Co.)

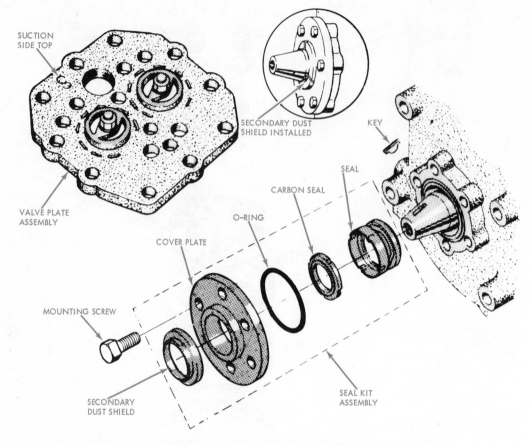

SUCTION
SIDE TOP

SECONDARY DUST
SHIELD INSTALLED

KEY

SEAL

CARBON SEAL

VALVE PLATE
ASSEMBLY

O-RING

COVER PLATE

MOUNTING SCREW

SECONDARY
DUST SHIELD

SEAL KIT
ASSEMBLY

Fig. 5-25. Compressor service—York compressor. (Ford Motor Co.)

plate or plates can then be removed. See Figs. 5-25 and 5-26.

If there is evidence of corrosion or metallic particles in the compressor, it should not be repaired, but replaced. If the compressor is clean, a replacement valve plate and gasket set can be obtained and installed if the old valve plate is damaged.

The valves are of the reed type and will fracture, leaving a piece of the valve loose in the head area. Always replace gaskets and seals with new ones and re-install and torque all bolts carefully. (Use torque values as specified by manufacturer or Table 5-2.) Take care to keep all parts clean.

This service can usually be performed with the compressor still on the engine.

G.M. Six Cylinder Compressor Replacement

It is not practical to repair the G.M. six cylinder compressor. The compressor can be disassembled by removing the four nuts which secure the rear cylinder head to the case. See Fig. 5-27. The oil pick-up tube can be easily pulled out and the in-

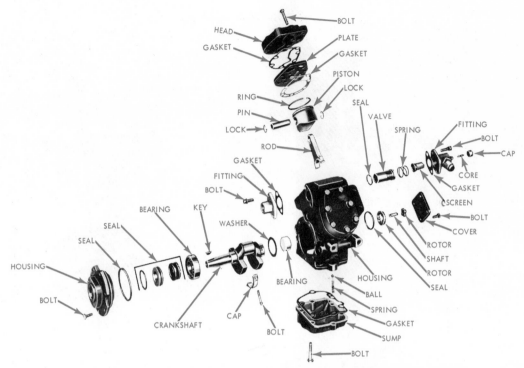

Fig. 5-26. Chrysler V-2 compressor disassembled. (Plymouth Div., Chrysler Corp.)

TABLE 5-2

Pipe and Hose Connection Torque Chart 1972 Olds Service Manual

METAL TUBE OUTSIDE DIAMETER	THREAD AND FITTING SIDE	STEEL TUBING TORQUE FT–LB	ALUMINUM OR COPPER TUBING TORQUE FT–LB	NOMINAL TORQUE WRENCH SPAN
1/4	7/16	10–15	5–7	5/8
3/8	5/8	30–35	11–13	3/4
1/2	3/4	30–35	15–20	7/8
5/8	7/8	30–35	21–27	1 1/16
3/4	1 1/16	30–35	28–33	1 1/4
If a connection is made with steel to aluminum or copper, use torques for aluminum In other words, use the lower torque specification				

ternal working mechanism can then be removed. A replacement cylinder and shaft assembly is available. The best procedure to follow is to exchange the compressor for a completely rebuilt unit. The cost of a compressor replacement is expensive, but repair is time consuming and does not always produce satisfactory results. See Fig. 5-28.

Follow the manufacturer's specifica-

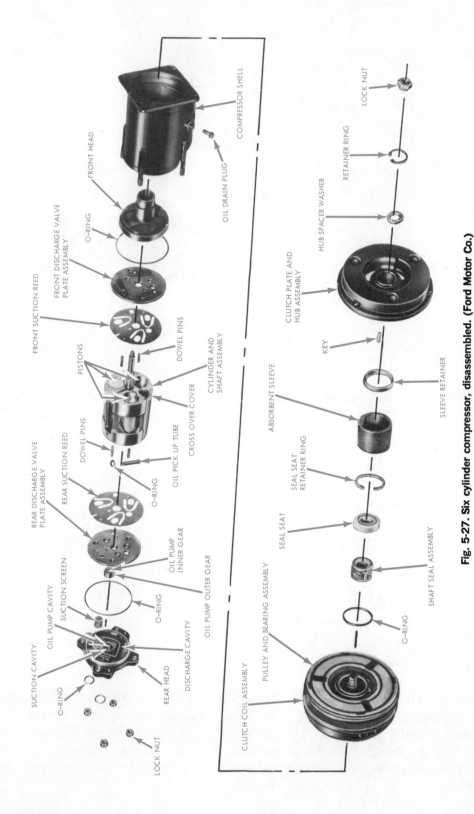

Fig. 5-27. Six cylinder compressor, disassembled. (Ford Motor Co.)

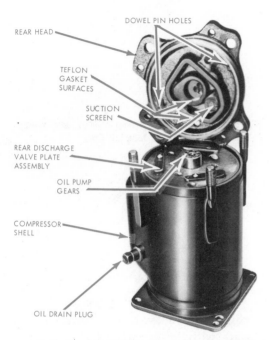

REAR HEAD

DOWEL PIN HOLES

TEFLON GASKET SURFACES

SUCTION SCREEN

REAR DISCHARGE VALVE PLATE ASSEMBLY

OIL PUMP GEARS

COMPRESSOR SHELL

OIL DRAIN PLUG

Fig. 5-28. Reed head being removed. (Ford Motor Co.)

as shown in Fig. 5-29. Steel or aluminum lines can be replaced by new lines of the same kind or they can be replaced with special metallic adapters or barbed fittings which will allow the use of a flexible hose. See Fig. 5-30. The important consideration when routing refrigerant lines is to keep them long enough so as to avoid sharp turns or bends. Always replace lines with lines of equivalent size. The liquid line will usually be smaller in diameter than the low-side lines. Avoid routing lines near exhaust manifolds. Secure hoses to prevent rubbing and chafing against sharp corners.

When separating fittings or lines, be sure that the system has been discharged. Use two wrenches so that the tubing will not become twisted or broken. Release

tions and procedures if further compressor service is to be attempted.

When installing a compressor, rotate the crankshaft by hand three or four complete turns to be certain no oil is trapped in the cylinder head area. After a vacuum pump-down, recharge the system and test for leaks.

It is suggested that a new receiver-drier be installed when any major component has been replaced or repaired. This provides maximum protection against moisture contamination that might occur if the old drier is used.

Hoses, Lines and Fittings

Hoses, lines and fittings are frequently sources of refrigerant leaks. Several methods of repair are available to stop leaks.

The flexible hose can be replaced or spliced with a special splice and clamps

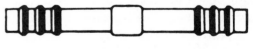

RUBBER HOSE SPLICE

NYLON HOSE SPLICE

Fig. 5-29. Splices and clamps can be used to repair hoses. A variety of sizes are available. (Essex International, Inc.)

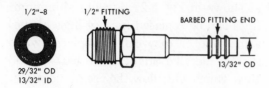

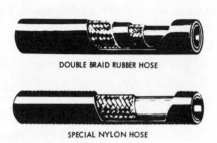

DOUBLE BRAID RUBBER HOSE

SPECIAL NYLON HOSE

Fig. 5-30. Freon hose, typical fittings, and O-ring. (Mark IV Div., John E. Mitchell Co.)

the fittings very slowly since some pressure might still remain even if the system has been discharged. Avoid using heat to loosen a tight connection.

CAUTION: Remember that poisonous gases are produced if R-12 comes in contact with a flame!

When replacing fittings which use O-rings, always use new O-rings and lubricate with refrigerant oil. Tighten fittings to correct torque values as specified by manufacturer. See Table 5-2. Keep all connections clean and capped when not connected.

Valves-in-Receiver

The valves-in-receiver (VIR) assembly can be disassembled so that individual components can be replaced. Fig. 5-31 is a disassembled view of the VIR unit. It is important to point out that all pressure must be released from the system before the VIR can be serviced. Once discharged, the connector shell can be removed to expose the POA and expansion valve. Fig. 5-32 shows how the expansion valve is lifted out with a special tool. Fig. 5-33 illustrates how the POA valve

can be removed with a special tool. It is advisable to replace the desiccant bag whenever the VIR is serviced or whenever a component is repaired or replaced. This VIR refrigeration control-valve assembly is presently the only one which utilizes a replaceable desiccant bag.

After repairs are made, the VIR is assembled using new O-rings and gaskets.

Note: the presence of oil on the outside of the VIR is considered normal as some seepage will occur. The VIR should

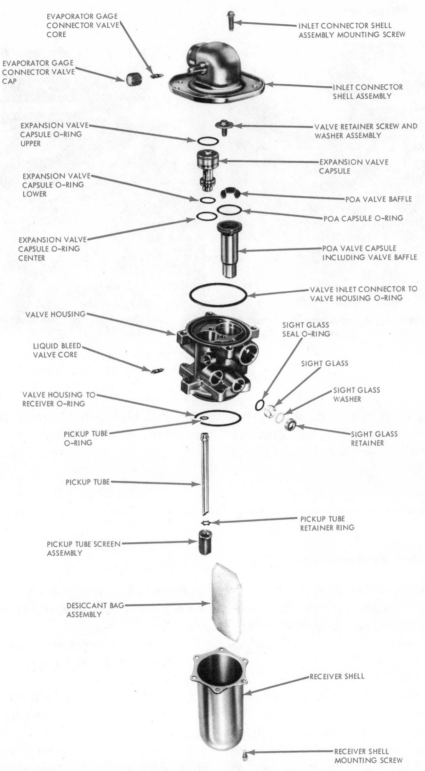

EVAPORATOR GAGE
CONNECTOR VALVE
CORE

INLET CONNECTOR SHELL
ASSEMBLY MOUNTING SCREW

EVAPORATOR GAGE
CONNECTOR VALVE
CAP

INLET CONNECTOR
SHELL ASSEMBLY

EXPANSION VALVE
CAPSULE O-RING
UPPER

VALVE RETAINER SCREW AND
WASHER ASSEMBLY

EXPANSION VALVE
CAPSULE

EXPANSION VALVE
CAPSULE O-RING
LOWER

POA VALVE BAFFLE

POA CAPSULE O-RING

EXPANSION VALVE
CAPSULE O-RING
CENTER

POA VALVE CAPSULE
INCLUDING VALVE BAFFLE

VALVE INLET CONNECTOR TO
VALVE HOUSING O-RING

VALVE HOUSING

SIGHT GLASS
SEAL O-RING

LIQUID BLEED
VALVE CORE

SIGHT GLASS

SIGHT GLASS
WASHER

VALVE HOUSING TO
RECEIVER O-RING

PICKUP TUBE
O-RING

SIGHT GLASS
RETAINER

PICKUP TUBE

PICKUP TUBE
RETAINER RING

PICKUP TUBE SCREEN
ASSEMBLY

DESICCANT BAG
ASSEMBLY

RECEIVER SHELL

RECEIVER SHELL
MOUNTING SCREW

Fig. 5-31. The valves-in-receiver disassembled. Note that the desiccant bag is replaceable. (Oldsmobile
Div., General Motors Corp.)

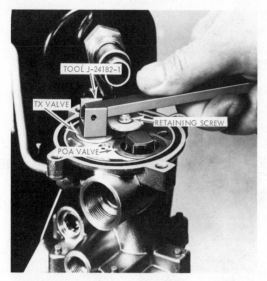

Fig. 5-32. Removing the expansion valve from the VIR. (Oldsmobile Div., General Motors Corp.)

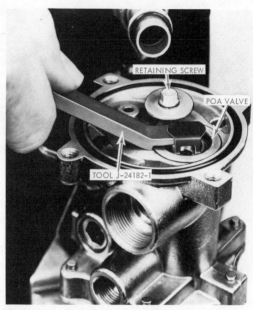

Fig. 5-33. Removal of the POA valves from the VIR unit. (Oldsmobile Div., General Motors Corp.)

not be serviced merely because of this accumulation of oil. This oily condition normally would be indicative of an R-12 leak since oil and R-12 are in combination in the air conditioning system.

Component Replacement

Component replacement involves discharging the system and carefully disconnecting the refrigerant lines as necessary. Mounting bolts and housings must be removed.

In the case of the expansion valve, it is very important to firmly install and insulate the temperature sensing bulb. The bulb is clamped to the evaporator tailpipe or inserted into a well-type cavity designed for the bulb. Insulation tape is provided to cover the expansion valve bulb so that it can properly sense the temperature of the gas leaving the evaporator. See Fig. 5-34.

When installation of any component is completed, always evacuate, recharge and leak-test the system.

Occasionally a system will be in need of flushing due to contamination. Air pressure is not recommended. Refrigerant can be used, but it is difficult to flush with liquid R-12. Flushing of evaporators, condensers and lines is best done with R-11

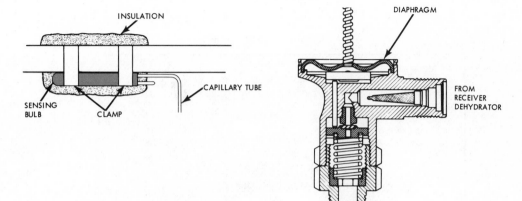

Fig. 5-34. Expansion valve connection to sensing bulb.

TABLE 5-3

TWO CYLINDER A/C COMPRESSOR SPECIFICATIONS

COMPRESSOR OIL CAPACITIES		
	VERTICAL	HORIZONTAL
Tecumseh [1]	7/8" min	7/8" min
11 fl oz	1 3/8" max	1 5/8" max
York [1]	7/8" min	13/16" min
10 fl oz	1 1/8" max	1 3/16" max
1 Do not add oil if dip stick indicates proper level of oil between minimum and maximum. If dip stick is below minimum level, add oil up to minimum oil level only		

TORQUE LIMITS (FT LBS)		
DESCRIPTION	TECUMSEH	YORK
Cylinder Head	20–24	15–23
Front Seal Plate	54–78 in-lb	7–13
Service Valve (Tube-O)	20+10	20+10
Mounting Bolt	20–30	20–30
Oil Filler Plug	18–22	4–11
Clutch Mounting	20–30	20–30
Base Plate		14–22
Back Plate		9–17
Compressor Clutch Run Out	1/32" max	

DRIVEN BELT TENSION	
New	140 lbs
Used [2]	90–110 lbs
2 A belt that has been operated for a minimum of 10 minutes is considered used	

TABLE 5–4

G.M. Compressor Specifications

COMPRESSOR	
Make	Frigidaire
Type	6 Cylinder Axial
Displacement	
Four-Season (Except Corvette) and Comfortron	12.6 cu in
Corvette Four-Season	10.8 cu in
Rotation	Clockwise
COMPRESSOR CLUTCH COIL	
Ohms (at 80°F)	3.70
Amps (at 80°F)	3.22 at 12 volts
TORQUE SPECIFICATIONS	
Compressor Suction and Discharge Connector Bolt	25 ft lbs
Rear Head to Shell Stud Nuts	23 ft lbs
Shaft Mounting Nut	15 ft lbs
Belt Tension	See Tune-Up Chart
SYSTEM CAPACITIES	
Refrigerant 12	
Four-Season (Except Corvette) and Comfortron Systems	3 lbs, 12 oz
Corvette Four-Season	3 lbs, 4 oz
525 Viscosity Compressor Oil	
All Systems	11 fl oz

BLOWER MOTOR

	Volts	Amps (Cold)	RPM (Cold)
	13–5		
Four-Season and Comfortron	12	16.5 Max	3700 Min

FUSES

	Fuse Block	In-Line
Four-Season	25 amp	30 amp
Comfortron	25 amp	30 amp

or dry compressed nitrogen gas. Either of these two is acceptable. The dry nitrogen will pick up moisture as flushing is performed. R-11 is a low-pressure refrigerant with properties similar to R-12. It is widely used as a flushing agent in refrigeration systems. It is easier to work with than R-12 because it is less active at normal temperatures. R-11 boils at approximately 75°F.

Compressors are frequently charged for shipment and storage with nitrogen gas which is much safer than refrigerant or air. Compressor specifications which are typical for most systems are given in Tables 5-3 and 5-4.

Problems to Consider

1. Remove a compressor clutch from a Ford or Chrysler type compressor. What are some conditions that could create difficulty in removing a clutch of this type?
2. Remove the clutch drive plate and pulley from a G.M. compressor. What are some problems to be expected? Could this be done with the compressor installed?
3. Check compressor drive belt condition and tension on several vehicles. Do any of these belts need adjustment or replacement?
4. Remove the compressor shaft seal from a G.M. compressor. Describe the steps necessary for removal and installation.
5. Remove a shaft seal from a York or Tecumseh compressor. Describe this operation.
6. Disassemble a compressor and examine how gas flows through it. Is there an oil pump in the compressor?
7. Disassemble a G.M. compressor. Examine how it operates. Does it use an oil pump?
8. Isolate a compressor (with service valves) and check the oil level. Release pressure slowly and after the oil level is checked, evacuate the compressor before opening the service valves.
9. Make a dipstick for your personal use.

Trade Competency Check

1. What are the typical indications of compressor clutch trouble?
2. When is it necessary to discharge the system for service?
3. When the pulley nut is removed, how is the compressor clutch removed on all but the six cylinder compressor?
4. What clearance should be maintained between the drive plate and pulley of a G.M. compressor?
5. Is it possible to replace a compressor shaft seal with the compressor mounted in the car?
6. What caution is necessary when handling compressor shaft seals?
7. List the steps necessary when replacing compressor shaft seals.
8. When is it necessary to check oil level in an air-conditioning system?
9. What is meant by an oil charge?
10. How is the oil level checked on a G.M. compressor?
11. What are the frequent types of compressor repairs that can be easily made?
12. Why should a compressor be rotated by hand before starting it with the engine?
13. When should a receiver-drier be replaced?
14. How can refrigerant lines be flushed?

Automatic Temperature Controls

Chapter 6 is designed to explain how the various types of automatic temperature control systems operate. The intent of this section is to provide a fundamental background of information for the automotive air-conditioning specialist. Because the systems are changed in small details from year to year and from model to model, no attempt is made to provide thorough coverage of all variations. A manufacturer's shop manual or training handbook for a specific model is necessary when servicing these rather complicated systems. With the information in this chapter, however, it is certainly much easier to comprehend how automatic temperature control can be achieved and how it functions.

Temperature Control Systems

Automatic temperature control, or ATC systems (as they are called when used on some cars) are being used more and more because they can provide and maintain a set comfort level within the vehicle with little or no change in control panel position. This is very convenient and does not require that the driver readjust or change control settings as the seasons change or as the weather varies.

Enough control is provided with automatic systems so that the operator is able to select the desired temperature range and make a choice of high or low blower speed. A provision is also made to provide for defrosting and de-icing when conditions exist which require them.

With an automatic system, the interior temperature is relatively constant regardless of the outside conditions. These systems will automatically deliver hot air at high blower speed on a cold morning. At the same time the system is able to provide cooled air if the outside temperature

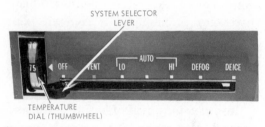

Fig. 6-1. Comfortron control head. (Chevrolet Div., General Motors Corp.)

increases during the day. Temperature control of this type can be achieved with a standard air conditioner also. The major difference is that, once set, all control in an automatic system is automatic and the driver does not need to reduce the blower speed, decrease or increase the temperature, or switch from heating to air conditioning. These *functions* (selecting heat or air conditioning) are performed by the various automatic system controls. The driver needs only to set the temperature desired and switch on the system.

Fig. 6-2. Comfortron engine compartment components. (Chevrolet Div., General Motors Corp.)

Automatic control is maintained in summer and winter. In hot weather the car will be cooled to the pre-set comfort

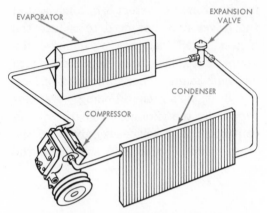

Fig. 6-3. The basic refrigeration system is unchanged. (Chrysler Corp.)

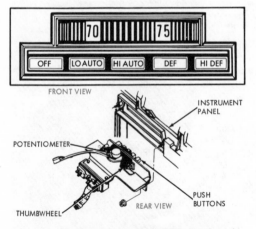

Fig. 6-4. Push-button control. (Chrysler Corp.)

level and will adjust itself to maintain comfort. In mild weather the vehicle will remain comfortable without any resetting of the control. On cold days a delay is provided which allows engine coolant to warm before the system operates. This is necessary to minimize a cold air blast from the heater outlets. The system will then heat the interior of the vehicle and level off or modulate when the comfort level is reached.

In order to provide for this automatic control of temperature, several special devices are used in addition to the standard air-conditioning and heating system. It is the purpose of these automatic controls to perform for the driver the adjustments he normally would need to make to provide interior comfort. See Figs. 6-1 and 6-2.

With a sound understanding of the operation of a manually-controlled heater and air conditioner, it is not at all difficult to understand the method of operation for the automatic units.

The heating and air conditioning components used in ATC systems are the same as those used in a standard or manual air conditioner. See Fig. 6-3. The changes which are made include a revised control panel, which normally will have two control levers. See Fig. 6-4. One lever

Fig. 6-5. Comfortron control. (Chevrolet Div., General Motors Corp.)

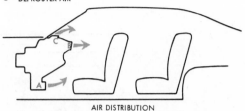

A – HEATER OUTLET AIR
B – A/C OUTLET AIR
C – DEFROSTER AIR

Fig. 6-6. Typical air flow for factory air-conditioning system. Automatic control positions shown. (Oldsmobile Div., General Motors Corp.)

AIR DISTRIBUTION

POSITION	OFF	VENT	LO	AUTO	HI	BI LEVEL	DE-FROST
A	100%	–	*	*	*	45%	15%
B	–	100%	*	*	*	50%	–
C	–	–	*	*	*	5%	85%

*AIR DISTRIBUTION VARIABLE

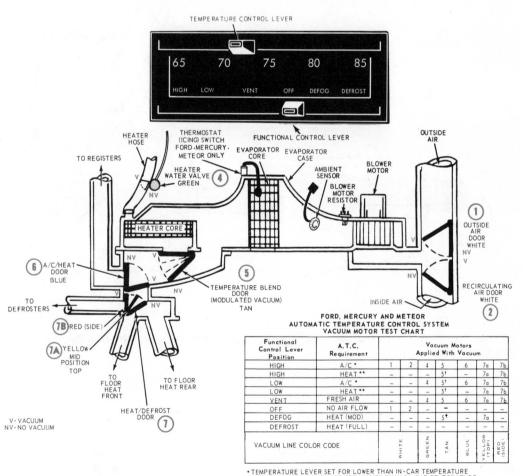

FORD, MERCURY AND METEOR
AUTOMATIC TEMPERATURE CONTROL SYSTEM
VACUUM MOTOR TEST CHART

Functional Control Lever Position	A.T.C. Requirement	Vacuum Motors Applied With Vacuum						
		1	2	4	5	6	7a	7b
HIGH	A/C *	1	2	4	5	6	7a	7b
HIGH	HEAT **	–	–	–	5†	–	7a	7b
LOW	A/C *	–	–	4	5†	6	7a	7b
LOW	HEAT **	–	–	–	5†	–	7a	7b
VENT	FRESH AIR	–	–	4	5	6	7a	7b
OFF	NO AIR FLOW	1	2	–	–	–	–	–
DEFOG	HEAT (MOD)	–	–	–	5†	–	7a	–
DEFROST	HEAT (FULL)	–	–	–	–	–	–	–
VACUUM LINE COLOR CODE		WHITE	GREEN	TAN	BLUE	YELLOW (TOP)	RED (SIDE)	

* TEMPERATURE LEVER SET FOR LOWER THAN IN-CAR TEMPERATURE
** TEMPERATURE LEVER SET FOR HIGHER THAN IN-CAR TEMPERATURE
†VACUUM MODULATES BETWEEN NO VACUUM AND FULL VACUUM

Fig. 6-7. System schematic and vacuum application chart. (Ford Motor Co.)

139

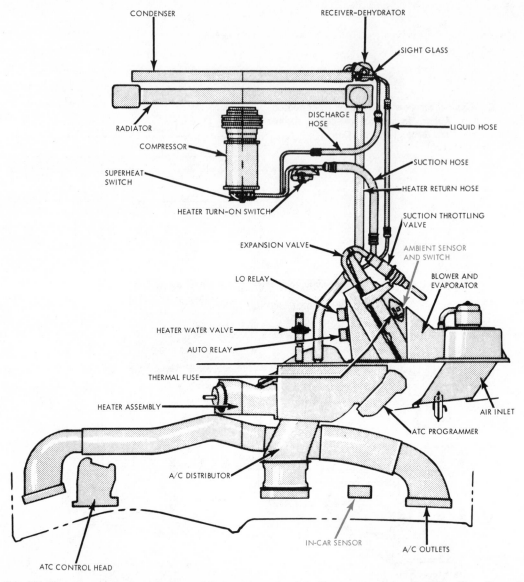

Fig. 6-8. The in-car sensor and the ambient sensor signal to the programmer. (Cadillac Div., General Motors Corp.)

is used to select the desired temperature. The range extends from 65°F to 85°F. This is a broad enough range to satisfy most human comfort desires. The normal setting for these units is considered to be 75°F. Some units will substitute numbers

1-6 instead of using a temperature numeral. See Fig. 6-5.

The other control lever is used to turn the system *on* or *off*. The normal ON positions are *high* or *low*, with some controls also including an automatic position between *low* and *high*. A few units also include a separate fan switch. In addition, this control lever will also provide for override of the automatic controls for de-icing and de-fogging during winter conditions. This provides the driver with greater choice of air flow and allows more air to flow from the defroster outlets. Normal operation in the automatic positions, however, would *not* provide the defroster air flow necessary to clear windows on winter days. See Fig. 6-6.

Probably most noticeable from the driver's standpoint is that there is no blower or fan switch. Blower speed is automatically controlled by a special device known as a programmer, an ATC box, or a power servo box. When the driver selects a position or function such as *high* on the control panel, a series of events are set into operation which will control blower speed according to the needs of the driver. See Fig. 6-7.

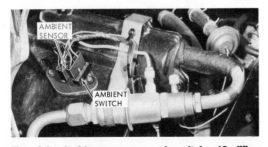

Fig. 6-9. Ambient sensor and switch. (Cadillac Div., General Motors Corp.)

Sensing Temperatures

When the outside temperature is high and the in-car temperature is high, air conditioning is necessary. The driver might select high range operation so as to speed up the cooling process. High and low range operation differ only in that high blower speeds are available in high range. The programmer or ATC box would then position the air flow doors for maximum cooling and place the blower at maximum speed. As the interior temperature begins to approach the temperature selected, the blower speed will be reduced and the air conditioner temperature door will be re-positioned to maintain the selected temperature. In order to perform in this manner the programmer or ATC box is supplied with a very small voltage signal from two sensors (ambient air sensor and in-car sensor), and the resistance value of the temperature selector lever on the control panel. See Fig. 6-8.

The ambient sensor is usually placed near or in the fresh air inlet door at the cowl air intake location. It is thus able to sense electrically the temperature of the outside or incoming ambient air. See Fig. 6-9.

The in-car sensor is located on the instrument panel. It is designed with an aspirator hose attached to the heater air flow ductwork. See Fig. 6-10.

As air flows past the hose, a vacuum is produced in the aspirator hose which causes air in the vehicle to be drawn past the in-car sensor, thus providing the system controls with an electrical sense of in-car temperature. See Fig. 6-11.

With ambient and in-car temperature sensed, the electrical value at the control head remains as the final link in a chain of events. The value at the control head

ASPIRATOR
HOSE PORT

IN-CAR SENSOR

Fig. 6-10. In-car sensor. (Chevrolet Div., General Motors Corp.)

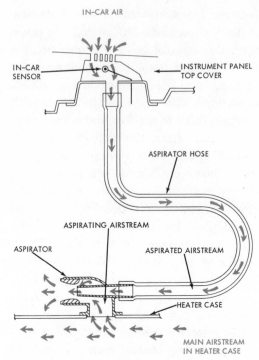

IN-CAR AIR

IN-CAR SENSOR

INSTRUMENT PANEL TOP COVER

ASPIRATOR HOSE

ASPIRATING AIRSTREAM

ASPIRATOR

ASPIRATED AIRSTREAM

HEATER CASE

MAIN AIRSTREAM IN HEATER CASE

Fig. 6-11. Operation of aspiration to direct in-car air over the in-car sensor. (Cadillac Div., General Motors Corp.)

is set by the driver. See Fig. 6-12. The sensors are electrically connected in series so that, with battery voltage applied to the sensor string, the resistance of the sensing wire is changed by the temperature of the air passing over it. This results in a small voltage which is not strong enough to do any controlling. This weak signal voltage is delivered to the control box where it is electronically increased, or amplified, to a proportionately larger value. When the sensor string voltage is amplified, further actions can be produced readily. See Figs. 6-13 and 6-14.

Transducer Action

The function door positions (heat, or air conditioning) are controlled by vacuum motors and servos. Automatic units use a vacuum-operated servo to operate the temperature blend door instead of a cable which is usually used with manual systems. The amplified sensor voltage is directed to a device known as a transducer. See Fig. 6-15. The transducer is able to produce a variable vacuum by altering the amount of electricity supplied to it. See Figs. 6-16 and 6-17. Sensor voltage, after amplification, is directed to the transducer, which changes the electrical value to a vacuum value. The regulated vacuum from the transducer is applied to a power servo.

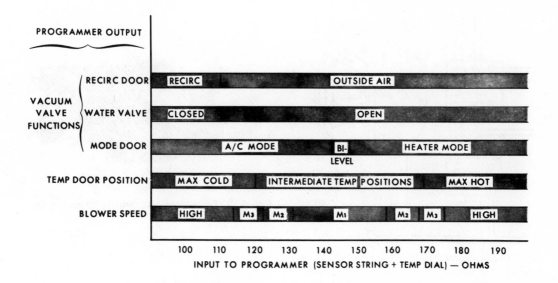

Fig. 6-12. Programmer input-output chart. (Cadillac Div., General Motors Corp.)

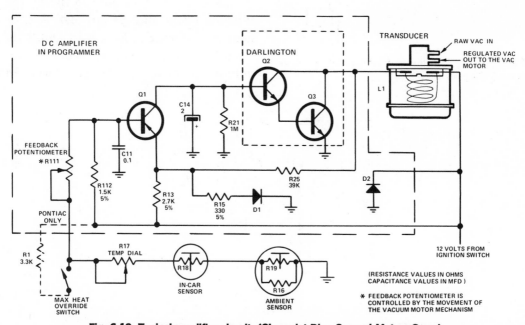

Fig. 6-13. Typical amplifier circuit. (Chevrolet Div., General Motors Corp.)

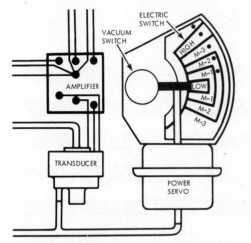

Fig. 6-14. Temperature signals control the amplifier. (Chrysler Corp.)

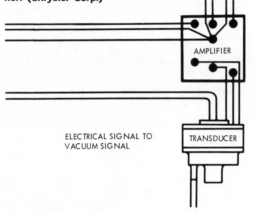

Fig. 6-15. A transducer transfers or changes power. (Chrysler Corp.)

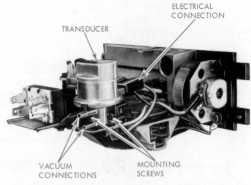

Fig. 6-17. Transducer installation. (Chevrolet Div., General Motors Corp.)

Power Servo

The power servo performs several tasks. The basic job is to position the temperature blend door properly. At the same time the blend door is being positioned, the power servo or programmer is also operating a rotary vacuum switch which supplies operating vacuum to the proper function doors, such as air inlet, A/C or heat or defrost. See Figs. 6-18 and 6-19. Vacuum at this switch is manifold vacuum not regulated by the transducer. As

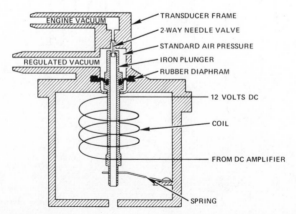

Fig. 6-16. Typical transducer. (Chevrolet Div., General Motors Corp.)

OUTPUT SHAFT

AMPLIFIER

FEEDBACK
POTENTIOMETER

TRANSDUCER

CHECKING
RELAY

PROGRAMMEI
VACUUM
VALVE

VACUUM
MOTOR

BLOWER
CIRCUIT
BOARD

VACUUM MOTOR MECHANISM

Fig. 6-18. Programmer used in G.M. systems. (Cadillac Div., General Motors Corp.)

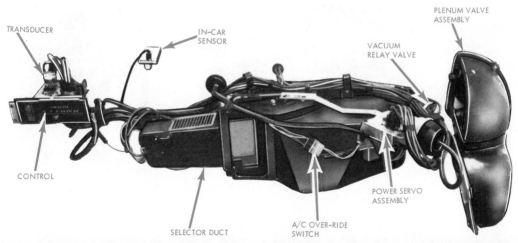

PLENUM VALVE
ASSEMBLY

TRANSDUCER

IN–CAR
SENSOR

VACUUM
RELAY VALVE

CONTROL

POWER SERVO
ASSEMBLY

SELECTOR DUCT

A/C OVER–RIDE
SWITCH

Fig. 6-19. Power servo operates the temperature blend door. A programmer is used on newer G.M. models. (Chevrolet Div., General Motors Corp.)

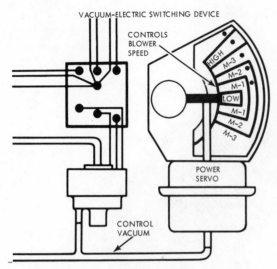

Fig 6-20. Transducer vacuum positions the power servo. (Chrysler Corp.)

the rotary switch is moved, blower speeds are also selected. See Fig. 6-20. This is accomplished by a sliding arm called the *wiper* which moves is conjunction with power servo movement. When the tem-

perature door is wide open or fully closed the wiper arm will make contact to provide the high blower speed needed for maximum cooling or maximum heating. As the temperature door moves toward a mid-position, the blower speeds are reduced by subsequent movement of the wiper arm. See Fig. 6-21.

De-icing

When the driver wants de-icing, moving the selector lever causes a relay to be energized, bypassing the normal control circuits and providing high blower speed and maximum air flow to the windshield. De-ice normally will only provide heated, high blower air flow. De-ice is an override of the automatic system which provides high speed defrosting.

De-fogging

De-fogging is also a bypass of normal controls. It provides for air flow to floor outlets and to the defroster nozzles. Tem-

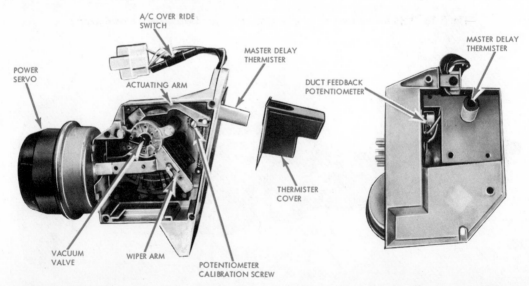

Fig. 6-21. Power servo with vacuum valve and wiper arm to control blower speeds. (Chevrolet Div., General Motors Corp.)

perature can be controlled with the temperature selector. In effect, de-fog operation is much like using a standard heater. Blower speeds are controlled automatically by the temperature requirements.

Cold Engine Delay

It is also desirable to prevent the automatic system from operating when heat is required and while the engine is cold. A water temperature switch is used to prevent system operation until coolant temperature has warmed sufficiently. This switch can be by-passed in the de-ice position. This switch will allow the unit to operate when the engine coolant temperature reaches approximately 125°F, which should occur after 3 to 5 minutes of operation.

Compressor Cut-out

When the automatic system is operating, the air-conditioning compressor will also be on at all times. The one exception is that the compressor will not operate when temperatures (ambient) are below approximately 40°F. An ambient switch is used to cut out or prevent the compressor clutch from operating. Do not confuse the *ambient switch* with the *ambient sensor* used to sense temperatures and to trigger the switch.

Vacuum Control

A vacuum check is used on G.M. cars to hold the power servo in its position when engine manifold vacuum has dropped off, which would upset the system's operation. This vacuum check will also hold when the engine has been stopped, to allow the air control system to resume its functioning without a complete recycling. A vacuum check valve

with a small vacuum reservoir tank is used on vehicles that do not use a vacuum check. The reservoir will supply vacuum to the system during periods of low engine vacuum and the check valve prevents loss of vacuum into the intake manifold when the engine stops.

When operating automatic systems, the response of the system to changes in switch positions or temperature selection is not immediate. Small restrictions are used in the vacuum supply line to cause the vacuum to be applied slowly, thus there is a slight response delay. This is desirable to prevent the system from shifting rapidly from one speed or mode to another and causing driver discomfort. See Figs. 6-22 and 6-23.

Chrysler System Variations

Chrysler Corporation cars control temperatures by using power servos that vary the amount of hot water flowing through the heater core. A temperature blend door is not used. When no amplifier power is applied to the power servo, no water will flow into the heater, and air discharged into the vehicle will be cooled by the evaporator, as in Fig. 6-24. Some systems will use a small electric motor to control the flow of water and to position a rotary vacuum switch and blower speed switch wiper arm. No transducer is used in this design. The servo motor operates through a set of small gears to achieve proper positioning.

As the interior becomes cool, power is supplied to the water valve which then admits a small amount of hot water to the heater core. See Fig. 6-25. As it passes over the heater core cool air from the evaporator is warmed before discharging into the passenger compart-

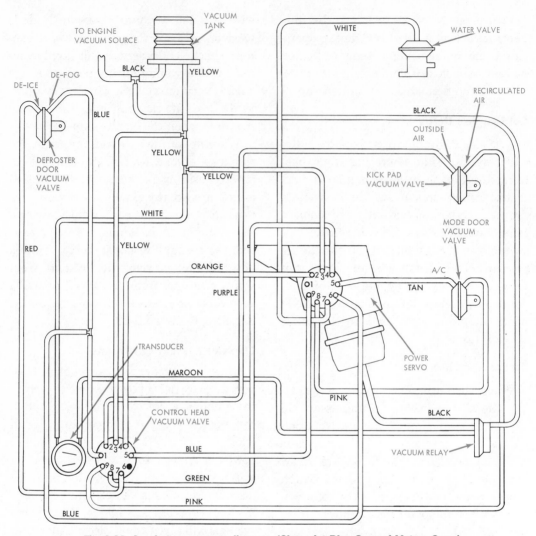

Fig. 6-22. Comfortron vacuum diagram. (Chevrolet Div., General Motors Corp.)

ment. Because of this design it is necessary that anti-freeze be used at all times to prevent a freeze-up of the heater core. This could occur in the summer if water were trapped in the heater core by a closed vacuum valve.

Ford System Variations

Ford Motor Company systems also have a slight modification of system operation as described earlier. Electric solenoid valves are used in place of a rotary vacuum switch. See Figs. 6-26 and 6-27.

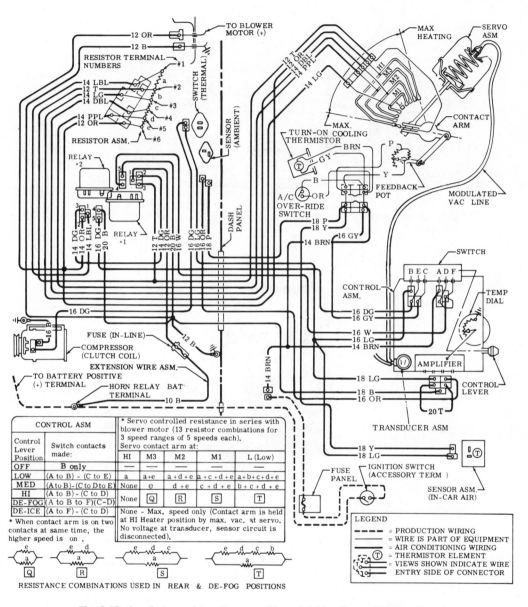

Fig. 6-23. Comfortron wiring diagram. (Chevrolet Div., General Motors Corp.)

The movement of the power servo, which positions the temperature blend door, then activates the vacuum motors by sending electrical power to the appropriate solenoid valve. Vacuum will be directed past the solenoid valve to the proper mode-door vacuum diaphragms. The power servo selects blower speeds as previously described. See Fig. 6-28.

The 1973 model Ford vehicles with ATC use a new method to provide a regulated vacuum to the power servo. This

149

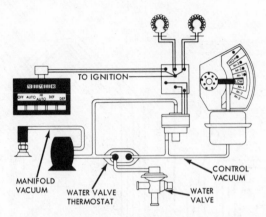

Fig. 6-24. In this system a water valve is separated from the power servo. (Chrysler Corp.)

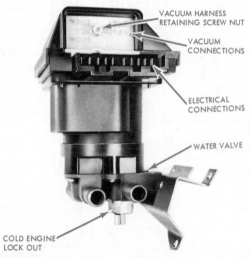

Fig. 6-25. Chrysler power servo assembly which controls temperature by regulating hot water into the heater (1971). (Chrysler Corp.)

control uses two strips of metal (bimetal sensor) for temperature sensing instead of electrical sensors. One bimetal sensor is used for in-car temperature sensing, and the second bimetal sensor senses ambient or outside air temperature. The two sensors are mechanically linked together and by their combined operation cause a modulated vacuum to be delivered to the power servo.

Because these sensors are mechanical rather than electrical the driver operated temperature control lever is also mechanical. As the desired temperature is se-

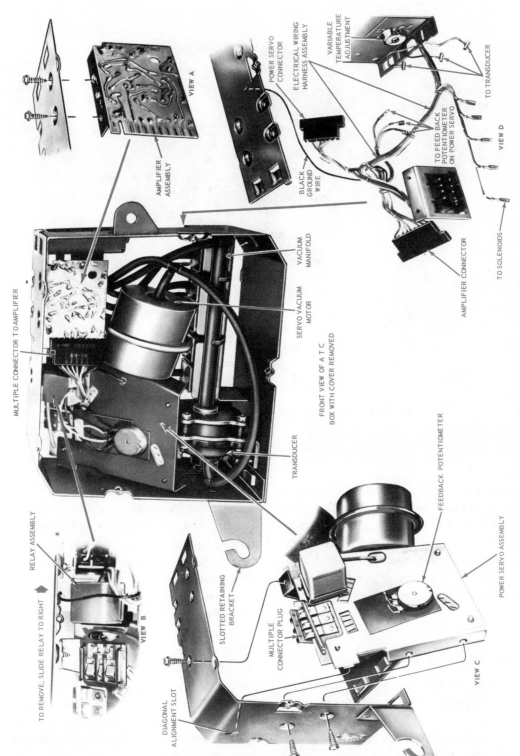

Fig. 6-26. Front view of Ford type ATC box. (Ford Motor Co.)

VIEW A

AMPLIFIER ASSEMBLY

POWER SERVO CONNECTOR

ELECTRICAL WIRING HARNESS ASSEMBLY

VARIABLE TEMPERATURE ADJUSTMENT

TO TRANSDUCER

BLACK GROUND WIRE

TO FEED BACK POTENTIOMETER ON POWER SERVO

VIEW D

TO SOLENOIDS

AMPLIFIER CONNECTOR

MULTIPLE CONNECTOR TO AMPLIFIER

VACUUM MANIFOLD

SERVO VACUUM MOTOR

FRONT VIEW OF A T C BOX WITH COVER REMOVED

TRANSDUCER

RELAY ASSEMBLY

TO REMOVE, SLIDE RELAY TO RIGHT

VIEW B

DIAGONAL ALIGNMENT SLOT

SLOTTED RETAINING BRACKET

MULTIPLE CONNECTOR PLUG

FEEDBACK POTENTIOMETER

POWER SERVO ASSEMBLY

VIEW C

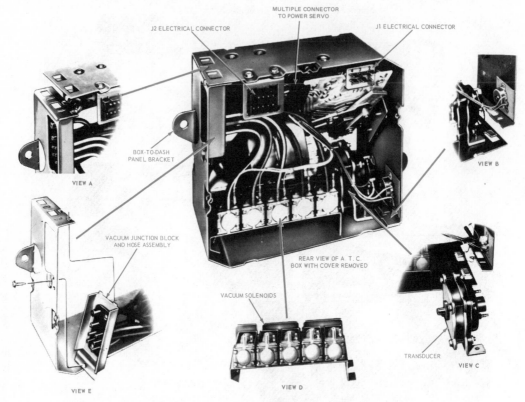

MULTIPLE CONNECTOR
TO POWER SERVO

J2 ELECTRICAL CONNECTOR

J1 ELECTRICAL CONNECTOR

BOX-TO-DASH
PANEL BRACKET

VIEW A

VIEW B

VACUUM JUNCTION BLOCK
AND HOSE ASSEMBLY

REAR VIEW OF A. T. C.
BOX WITH COVER REMOVED

VACUUM SOLENOIDS

TRANSDUCER

VIEW C

VIEW E

VIEW D

Fig. 6-27. Rear view of Ford type ATC box. (Ford Motor Co.)

lected, a cable is operated which is connected to the sensor assembly. The cable travel gives the sensor a set point from which the sensors can provide automatic regulation to maintain the desired temperature. The sensor is located behind the trim panel of the dashboard.

Evaporator Icing Control

As part of the design for temperature control, whenever the system is operating above 40°F the compressor will operate. Automatic systems will cool outside air and re-heat the cooled air to provide the selected interior temperature.

Provision needs to be made to control icing on the evaporator in any air-conditioning system. Automatic units, because they run the compressor at lower ambient temperatures, require control of evaporator pressure to prevent evaporator icing. The G.M. system called *Comfortron* uses the POA valve described in Chapter 4 to prevent evaporator freeze-up. Ford systems use the icing switch to turn off the compressor if evaporator temperature is close to the freezing point of moisture. Some Ford vehicles use the G.M. POA valve to allow for continuous operation of the compressor.

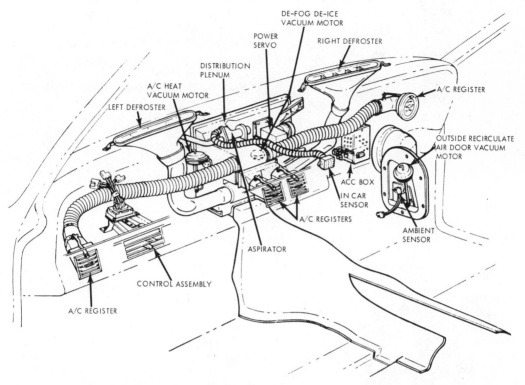

Fig. 6-28. Automatic climate control assembly. (Ford Motor Co.)

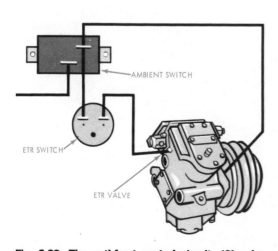

Fig. 6-29. The anti-frost control circuit. (Chrysler Corp.)

Chrysler cars, which normally use the evaporator pressure regulator (EPR) valve, replaced the EPR valve with an evaporator temperature regulator (ETR). See Fig. 6-29. The ETR is an electrical solenoid switch which shuts off refrigerant flow into the compressor. See Fig. 6-30. It serves the same purpose as the EPR valve except that it is electrically operated rather than pressure operated as is the EPR valve. The ETR solenoid is located in the compressor. See Fig. 6-31. It is controlled by an ETR switch located at the evaporator and can sense low evaporator temperature. See Figs. 6-32 and 6-33.

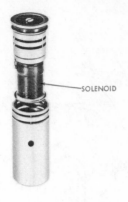

SOLENOID

Fig. 6-30. The ETR valve. (Chrysler Corp.)

TOOL

Fig. 6-31. Removing the ETR valve. (Chrysler Corp.)

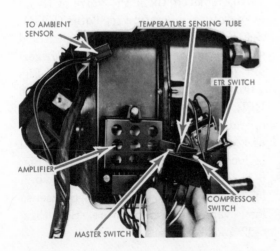

TO AMBIENT SENSOR

TEMPERATURE SENSING TUBE

ETR SWITCH

AMPLIFIER

COMPRESSOR SWITCH

MASTER SWITCH

Fig. 6-32. Amplifier and ETR switch location. (Chrysler Corp.)

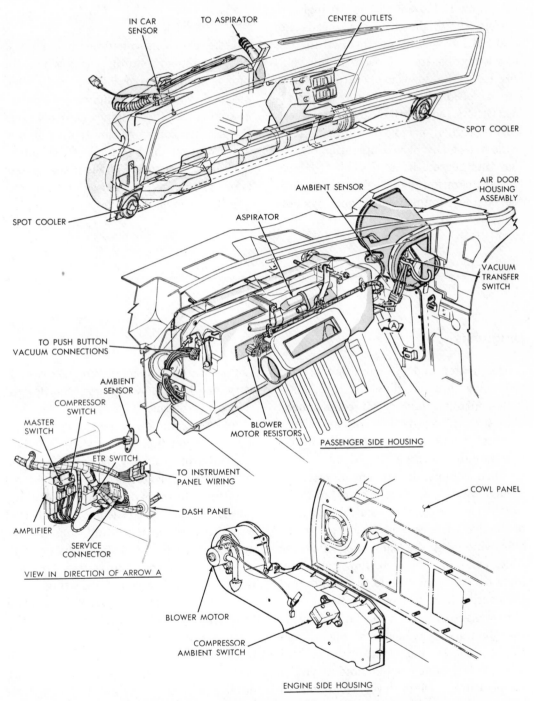

IN CAR SENSOR

TO ASPIRATOR

CENTER OUTLETS

SPOT COOLER

SPOT COOLER

AMBIENT SENSOR

AIR DOOR HOUSING ASSEMBLY

ASPIRATOR

VACUUM TRANSFER SWITCH

TO PUSH BUTTON VACUUM CONNECTIONS

AMBIENT SENSOR

COMPRESSOR SWITCH

MASTER SWITCH

ETR SWITCH

TO INSTRUMENT PANEL WIRING

BLOWER MOTOR RESISTORS

PASSENGER SIDE HOUSING

AMPLIFIER

SERVICE CONNECTOR

DASH PANEL

VIEW IN DIRECTION OF ARROW A

COWL PANEL

BLOWER MOTOR

COMPRESSOR AMBIENT SWITCH

ENGINE SIDE HOUSING

Fig. 6-33. Location of ATC component at cowl. (Chrysler Corp.)

Blower Operation

Automatic systems will usually have five available blower speeds. In high operation, the highest blower speeds are used. In low operation, the two highest blower speeds are not used. Many vehicles have the blower operating at the lowest speed when the engine is operating. Others require that the system controls be turned or moved to an operating mode before any blower operation occurs. For this reason it is possible to have blower operation and air flow (low) with the engine running when some systems are switched *off*. This should not be diagnosed as a defective system.

Purge Doors

G.M. cars will sometimes use a purge door in the evaporator case. When the unit is off, the purge door opens to allow air to flow past the evaporator and discharge into the engine compartment. Purging is used to eliminate an unpleasant initial air-discharge odor from entering the passenger area. When the system is on, the purge door closes and a better quality air is delivered into the vehicle.

Diagnosis

The heater and air conditioner units themselves are not different from manually-controlled factory air conditioners. The sensors, control head, amplifier, transducer and power servo are additions to manually controlled units.

When complaints are encountered, it is necessary to verify the complaint and isolate the location or possible location of the difficulty. Special testers are available which can be connected into the ATC system. These testers can then force the automatic units to operate and thus verify their proper operation.

Before resorting to a special tester it is wise to make a visual and operational check of the system. Operate the control lever in each mode position, and move the temperature selector lever from low to high ranges and observe whether: (1) air temperatures change, (2) blower speeds vary, or (3) air flow changes according to selector positions.

As an example, a good system on a warm day on high range should deliver cool air from the A/C outlets when the temperature selected is 65°F. As the temperature selector is turned to 85°F, the air flow should switch to the floor outlets and a progressive decrease and then an increase of blower speed should be noticed. This indicates that the transducer, sensors, and power servo are operating.

Performance of the system is checked by driving the vehicle at 40 mph with the temperature selector at 75°F on high range. A thermometer should be taped near the in-car sensor. An in-car reading of 80°F with the lever set at 75 is operating as designed.

It is not always easy to gain access to the automatic control units, so a careful diagnosis is very important.

Maintenance

Maintenance of the automatic systems requires only a check to be certain all components are connected properly. A check of the sight glass when the compressor is operating will help determine if a refrigerant loss occurred. The engine cooling system, belts, and hoses should be properly adjusted and in good condition.

No specific maintenance is necessary if the system is operating properly. If improper operation is claimed by the driver, a thorough check should be made to determine if a problem exists. Many times a driver will complain because of a lack of understanding of how the automatic system operates.

Trouble Shooting

A logical procedure is necessary to determine if there is a problem. Before a

AUTOMATIC TEMPERATURE CONTROL FUNCTIONAL TEST

CONTROL SETTINGS	SYSTEM SHOULD OPERATE AS FOLLOWS:
DEF DIAL AT 85°	Air should be delivered out of defrost outlets at a fixed high blower speed Some air bleeds out of floor heater
BI-LEVEL DIAL AT 75°	Air should be delivered from both the A/C and heater outlets at a reduced blower speed Only a small portion of air will come out the defrost outlet
HI DIAL AT 65°	Air should be delivered out the A/C outlets at a fixed high blower speed and cool to cold temperature The recirculating air door should open (blower noise increases) Door movement will be slow because of vacuum delay plug
AUTO DIAL AT 65°	After 45 seconds the A/C discharge air should drop to 50°F or lower (may be slightly higher in 90°F or above ambients) Recirc air door should close (noise level will drop)
AUTO DIAL AT 85°	Blower speeds should drop (Hi – M^3 – M^2 – M^1 – etc.) and discharge air temperature should increase Depending on the temperature in the work area, the air delivery mode should change from the A/C outlets to the heater outlets
LO DIAL AT 85°	Air should be delivered at a fixed low blower speed
VENT DIAL AT 85°	Air should be discharged from the A/C outlets at a fixed low blower speed The A/C compressor should not operate
OFF DIAL AT 65°	Air should be discharged out the heater outlet at a fixed low blower speed No A/C compressor operation

Fig. 6-34. Procedure to follow to locate areas where malfunction occurs. (Cadillac Div., General Motors Corp.)

procedure can be followed, it is of utmost importance to understand how the system operates. Observation of how the system responds to various selector lever positions is necessary so that a specific problem area can be isolated. Generally, the procedure will involve pinpointing the source of trouble to a major component of the control system. The master control panel, a sensor, vacuum system, electrical system or the power servo (ATC box or programmer) are the main areas where troubles can occur.

At this point in trouble shooting the automatic system, a general area of trouble will usually be isolated, and specific tests can be performed to determine what is to be repaired or replaced, Fig. 6-34.

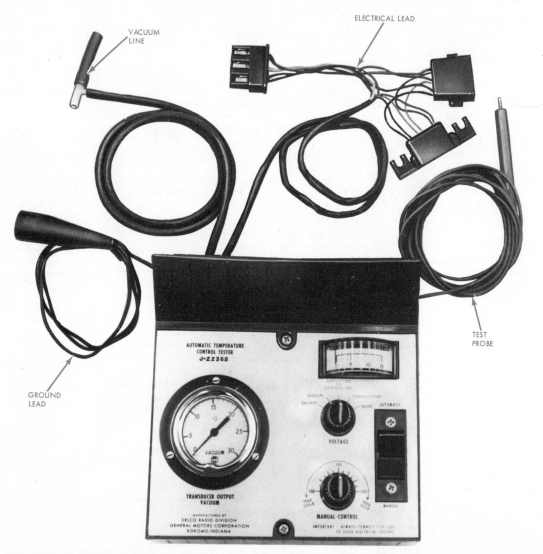

Fig. 6-35. Comfortron system tester for G.M. units without programmer. (Chevrolet Div., General Motors Corp.)

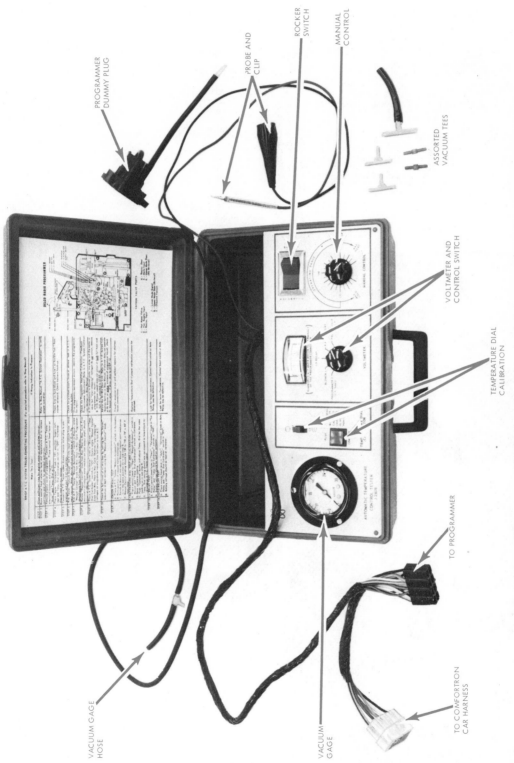

PROGRAMMER DUMMY PLUG

PROBE AND CLIP

ROCKER SWITCH

MANUAL CONTROL

ASSORTED VACUUM TEES

VOLTMETER AND CONTROL SWITCH

TEMPERATURE DIAL CALIBRATION

VACUUM GAGE HOSE

VACUUM GAGE

TO PROGRAMMER

TO COMFORTRON CAR HARNESS

Fig. 6-36. Comfortron tester for G.M. systems with programmer. (Chevrolet Div., General Motors Corp.)

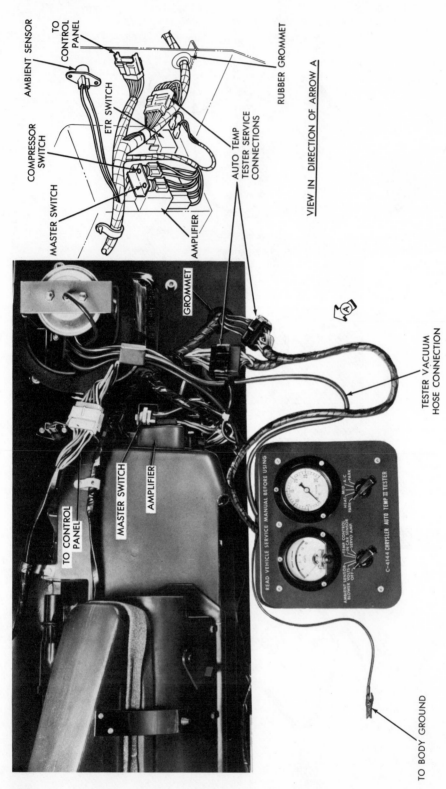

AMBIENT SENSOR

TO CONTROL PANEL

COMPRESSOR SWITCH

ETR SWITCH

MASTER SWITCH

AMPLIFIER

AUTO TEMP TESTER SERVICE CONNECTIONS

RUBBER GROMMET

VIEW IN DIRECTION OF ARROW A

GROMMET

TO CONTROL PANEL

MASTER SWITCH

AMPLIFIER

TESTER VACUUM HOSE CONNECTION

READ VEHICLE SERVICE MANUAL BEFORE USING

HEAT-MID A.C.

PART PARK

TEMP CONTROL CAB SENSOR SERVO AMP.

AMBIENT SENSOR VOLTS BLOWER OFF

C-4144 CHRYSLER AUTO TEMP II TESTER

TO BODY GROUND

Fig. 6-37. Auto-Temp tester connections. (Chrysler Corp.)

To facilitate these tests, the use of a system tester is recommended. Each system requires a different test unit, which can substitute various operations and functions, thus forcing the system to perform in specific modes. See Figs. 6-35, 6-36 and 6-37.

It is possible to check electrical

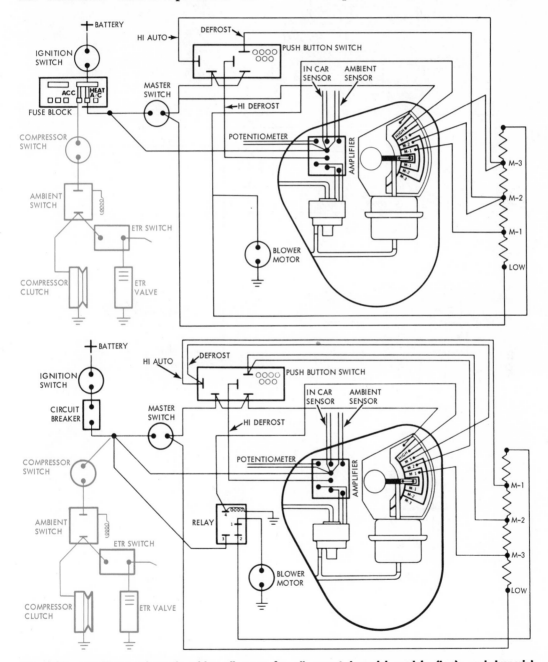

Fig. 6-38. Auto-Temp schematic wiring diagram for all except Imperial models (top); and Imperial schematic (bottom). (Chrysler Corp.)

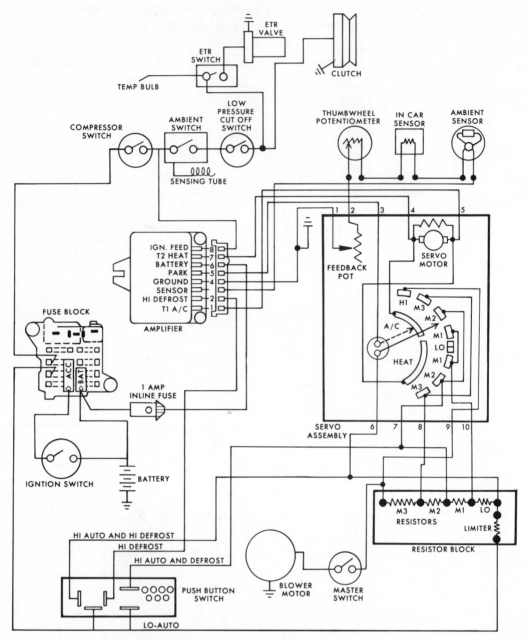

Fig. 6-39. Auto-Temp II wiring diagram. (Chrysler Corp.)

switches and relays in a conventional manner using a test light or continuity tester. The temperature selector is a variable resistor and can be checked with an ohmmeter to determine that it is continuous and will vary in resistance throughout its operating range.

In-car and ambient sensors also can be checked with an ohmmeter. A sensor will either be shorted, giving a very low reading on the ohmmeter, or the sensor could be open, which will cause the ohmmeter to register very high resistance. If a sensor is suspected, a substitute should be used to confirm that the sensor was defective.

A quick check of power servo operation can be performed by removing the vacuum hose at the power servo. Chrysler and G.M. systems will go to maximum cooling and high blower speed with the servo vacuum at zero. See Figs. 6-38 and 6-39.

When a Ford system servo is at zero vacuum, the system provides full heat and maximum blower speed. By removing the vacuum hose to the servo and noting operating conditions, servo operation can be confirmed without a tester. Teeing a vacuum gage into the servo vacuum line can provide information that the sensor string, amplifier, and transducer are functioning. A variation in vacuum will be noted when the temperature selector is moved from 65 to 85.

These types of quick checks can establish whether further testing is necessary or that the system is responding correctly as designed.

The use of a manufacturer's shop manual is very helpful for tests of specific systems. Each vehicle manufacturer, from year to year, will incorporate or delete certain electrical or vacuum controls. See Fig. 6-40.

The fundamental principles of *how* and *why* the automatic system operates will not change drastically. In order to improve control and efficiency, minor changes may be expected from year to year, and from one manufacturer to another.

Component Service

Most of the special units, such as control head, sensors, transducer, amplifier, power servo, vacuum valves and solenoid valves will require replacement if they are found to be operating improperly.

One basic adjustment, related to the control head, involves the calibration of the temperature dial or lever. Fig. 6-41 shows a typical procedure using a special tool to reset the temperature dial. The tool is used to prevent the dial shaft from turning. With the shaft held with the tool, the dial numerals can be repositioned to achieve the appropriate setting. This adjustment is necessary when the controlled temperature of the vehicle is above or below the temperature indicated on the dial. As an example, if the temperature in the car is 85°F at the in-car sensor and the temperature lever indicates a 70°F setting, a calibration is needed if all other components are operating properly. A system tester is necessary to make this adjustment properly.

Fig. 6-42 is an electrical diagram which is typical of a Lincoln automatic temperature control system, and which will allow you to trace all connections.

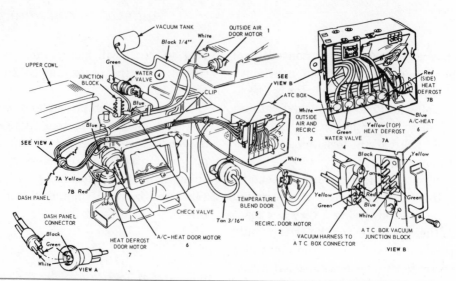

Fig. 6-40. Trouble-shooting chart for Ford ATC system. (Ford Motor Co.)

TEST	OPERATION	VISUAL-AUDIBLE CHECK
EQUIPMENT	1. Disconnect the vacuum connector from the ATC box	
1 – Jumper wire (14–16 gage) 3' to 6' long with alligator clip on one end, two C7AB–14488–B female pin terminals and one B9A–14294–L female spade terminal connectors on other end	2. Connect short vacuum supply jumper hose between the vacuum harness and the ATC box (S black)	
1 – Jumper wire (14–14 gage) 3' long with alligator clip on one end and one C7AB–14488–B female pin terminal connector on the other	3. Disconnect the brown and black electrical connectors from ATC box	
	4. Make sure the ATC box is grounded	
1 – Jumper wire for ground, 3' to 6' long with alligator clip on each end	5. Test the box with a minimum of 13 inches of vacuum	INDICATES SATISFACTORY PERFORMANCE
4 – Vacuum gages, or	NOTE: All vacuum connections should be connected before the electrical circuits are energized	
1 – Vacuum gage and		
3 – Vacuum motors		
1 – Ohmmeter, or		
1 – Self-powered test light		
1 – 12 volt test light		
3 – 1/8" x 1' vacuum hose		
1 – 3/16" x 1' vacuum hose		
1 – 1/4" x 1' vacuum hose		
1 – 383001–S vacuum connector (3/16" to 1/8")		
1 – 383005–S vacuum connector (1/4" to 1/4")		
1 Check defrost solenoid D2 Ability of box to operate defrost portion of heat-defrost vacuum motor 7B	Connect vacuum gage to D2 port on box Apply 12 volts to terminal 2 on box (brown connector) or Apply 12 volts to terminal of defrost (yellow solenoid)	Vacuum port D2 should go to full vacuum
2 Check de-fog solenoid D1 Ability of box to operate de-fog portion of heat-defrost vacuum motor 7A	Connect vacuum gage to D1 port on box Apply 12 volts to terminal pin 5 on box (brown connector) or Apply 12 volts to terminal of de-fog (red) solenoid	Vacuum port D1 should go to full vacuum

3 Check inlet door solenoid 1	Connect vacuum gage to I port vacuum connector on box	Vacuum port I should go to full vacuum
Ability of box to operate outside air door vacuum motor 1 and recirc door vacuum motor 2	Apply 12 volts to terminal pin 3 on box (brown connector) or Apply 12 volts to terminal of inlet (white) solenoid	
4 Check operation of cold engine water blower cut-off relay (inlet solenoid circuit)	Connect vacuum gage to D1 gage or motor to I port of vacuum connector on box	Vacuum port D1 should go to full vacuum
	Apply 12 volts to terminal pin 5 (brown connector) and spade terminal 6 (black connector)	Vacuum port I should go to zero vacuum
Ability of cold engine relay in box to override Step 3	Ground terminal pin 4 (brown connector)	Port I should go to full vacuum
5 Check cold engine relay (blower circuit)	Apply 12 volts to terminal pin 5, ground terminal pin 4 (brown connector)	Electrical continuity should cease between 5 and 6 spade terminals (black connector) (Use ohmmeter or self-powered test light)
Ability of cold engine relay in box to interrupt heater blower circuit	Remove ground from terminal pin 4 (brown connector)	Continuity should exist between 5 and 6 spade terminals (black connector)
6 Check amplifier and transducer	Connect vacuum gage to T port of vacuum connector on box	Vacuum port T should go to full vacuum
Ability of amplifier in box to call for full vacuum through transducer. If OK, proceed to Step 7	Apply 12 volts to terminal pin 7 and ground terminal pin 8 (brown connector)	Power servo switch arm must move from extreme right to extreme left (full vacuum) in about 5 seconds
	With 12 volts still applied to pin 7 and ground connected to pin 8 also apply 12 volts to pin 6 (brown connector)	Vacuum port T should go to zero vacuum Power servo switch arm must return from extreme left (full vacuum) to extreme right (zero vacuum) position
6a Check transducer	Connect vacuum gage to T port of vacuum connector on box	Vacuum port T should go to full vacuum
Ability of transducer to control vacuum supply to temperature blend door 5 and power servo modulating vacuum motors	Disconnect wire harness 1, 2 and 3 pin connectors from transducer. Connect fused (1/4 amp) + 12 volts to terminal pin 2 on transducer ground clip of 12 volt test light to frame of box and touch probe to terminal pin 1 of transducer	Power servo switch arm must move from extreme right (zero vacuum) to extreme left (full vacuum) in about 5 seconds When probe of 12 volt test light is removed, vacuum must maintain for an indefinite period of time (no leakage)
	Touch probe of 12 volt test light to terminal pin 3 of transducer	Vacuum port T should go to zero vacuum Power servo switch arm must move from extreme left (full vacuum) to extreme right (zero vacuum) in about 5 seconds
7 Check mode door M and water valve W solenoids	Install vacuum gage on port T of vacuum connector and motors or gages on D1, M and W ports	Vacuum ports T, D1, M, and W should go to full vacuum
	Apply 12 volts to terminal pins 7 and 5, and then ground terminal pin 8 (brown connector)	
Ability of box to operate A/C-heat door 6 and heater water valve 4 vacuum motors	Remove ground from terminal pin 8 (brown connector)	Vacuum ports T, M and W should go to zero vacuum and D1 remain at full vacuum
If the ATC box fails to pass any one of the above tests, the box is bad and should be repaired or replaced	Connect vacuum harness connector to box	
If the box passes all the tests, there is probably trouble elsewere in the system	Connect both brown (pin) and black (spade) electrical connectors to box	

Fig. 6-40. Trouble-shooting chart for Ford ATC system. (Ford Motor Co.)

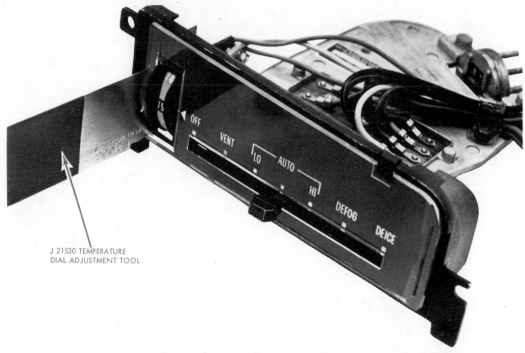

J 21530 TEMPERATURE
DIAL ADJUSTMENT TOOL

Fig. 6-41. Temperature dial calibration. (Chevrolet Div., General Motors Corp.)

Problems to Consider

1. Examine the engine compartment of a vehicle equipped with automatic temperature control. Sketch the layout, and note the locations of as many of the ATC components as you can.
2. Make a system operational test. Report your results and conclusions.
3. Locate and disconnect the temperature door vacuum hose. With the temperature door vacuum off, what is the effect on operation?
4. Using components from an ATC system, carefully examine their construction, and explain the purpose for each device.
5. Check the resistance of several sensors. Place the sensors in a cooler or a warmer environment. What is the effect on sensor resistance?
6. Make a list of the special devices used for an ATC. In your own words, define each item.

Trade Competency Check

1. How does the control panel of an automatic temperature control unit differ from a standard A/C system?
2. How is blower speed controlled in an automatic system?
3. How many sensors are usually used in an automatic system?
4. What device positions the air flow doors on

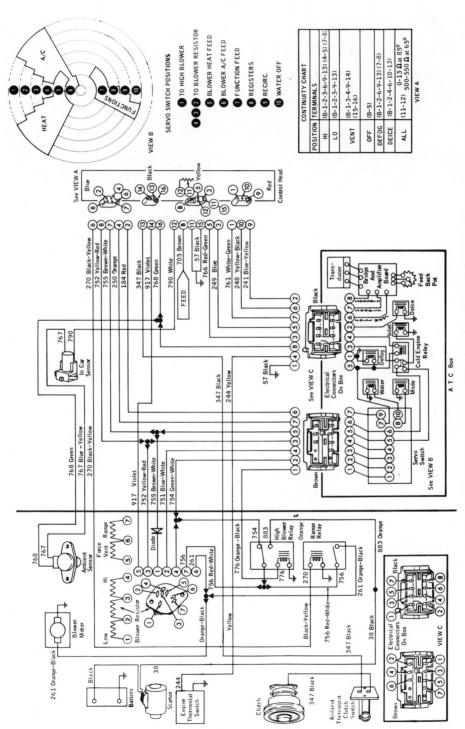

Fig. 6-42. Lincoln ATC system electrical schematic (1970). (Ford Motor Co.)

an automatic system?

5. What is the purpose of the aspirator used with the in-car sensor?

6. What is the purpose of a transducer?

7. What must be done to the sensor string voltage before it can be used?

8. If the temperature door is fully opened or fully closed, what blower speed is used?

9. What is the purpose of the *de-ice* function?

10. Why is a *de-fog* function provided?

11. Why would an automatic system, when set on high/automatic not start to operate for three to five minutes of engine operation?

12. What is the purpose of the vacuum check on G.M. products?

13. Does the compressor operate at all times with the automatic systems?

14. How is temperature controlled with a Chrysler automatic system?

15. Ford Motor automatic systems use small solenoid valves in the ATC box, for what reason?

16. What is the purpose of the ETR valve?

17. What steps should be followed when troubleshooting automatic systems?

18. How can an ohmmeter be used to test a sensor?

19. What kind of service is possible to major components of the automatic systems?

Glossary of
Air Conditioning Terms

A

absolute humidity: The actual amount of water vapor in a given volume of air; for example, grams of water per cubic foot of air.

absolute pressure: A pressure scale having as its zero point the complete absence of pressure. Atmospheric pressure on the absolute scale is 14.7 psi or 29.92 inches of mercury ("Hg).

absolute zero: The complete absence of heat which would occur at zero degrees absolute or minus 460 degrees Fahrenheit.

ambient temperature: The temperature of the surrounding air, such as room temperature, or outside temperature.

atmospheric pressure: The pressure on all objects in the atmosphere due to the height of the air which makes up the atmosphere. Atmospheric pressure at sea level is 14.7 psi absolute and decreases as altitude increases.

B

boiling: Conversion from the liquid to vapor state, which takes place throughout the liquid and is accompanied by bubbling as the vapor below the surface rises.

British thermal unit (Btu): The amount of heat necessary to raise the temperature of one pound of liquid water one degree Fahrenheit. The measure of heat quantity. 1 Btu = 778 pound feet or 252 calories.

C

calorie: A measure of heat quantity. The amount of heat needed to raise the temperature of one gram of water one degree Centigrade.

capillary tube: A tube with a very small inside diameter.

coefficient of expansion: The percent of increase in length per degree of temperature rise. An aluminum bar lengthens 13 millionths percent of the original length for each degree (F) of temperature rise.

cold: The absence of heat.

compression: Reducing the volume of gas by squeezing it into a smaller space. Increased pressure and temperature always accompany compression.

compressor: A machine for squeezing a vapor into a smaller space so as to raise the vapor pressure and temperature.

condensation: Conversion from the vapor to the liquid state.

condenser: A heat exchanger in which a vapor is changed to the liquid state by removing heat from the vapor.

conduction: The transfer of heat between the closely packed molecules of a substance or between two substances that are touching.

convection: The transfer of heat by motion of the heated material. Moving currents of a liquid or gas because of heat are called convection currents.

corrosion: Chemical action, usually by an acid, that decomposes a metal.

D

dehumidify: To remove water vapor from the air.

desiccant: A material which can absorb and hold moisture.

discharge pressure: Pressure at the compressor outlet (head pressure).

E

energy: The ability or capacity to do work; usually measured in work units (pound-feet), but also expressed in terms of heat energy (Btu's).

evaporation: Conversion from the liquid to the vapor state at the surface of the liquid only; it can occur at temperatures below the boiling point.

evaporator: A heat exchanger in which the liquid refrigerant absorbs heat and boils; the heat is transferred to the refrigerant from the air passing over the evaporator.

expansion valve. A metering device that controls the amount of refrigerant sprayed into the evaporator and controls expansion of the refrigerant in the evaporator.

F

fluid: Any liquid or gas.

force: Any push or pull exerted on an object; measured in units of weight, pounds, ounces, etc.

Freon: The trade name for the refrigerant R-12 ($C Cl_2 F_2$) dichlorodifluoromethane.

fusion: Melting; a conversion from a solid to a liquid state.

G

gage pressure: A reading of a pressure scale which ignores atmospheric pressure; atmospheric pressure of 14.7 psi absolute is zero psi, gage.

H

head pressure: Pressure at the compressor outlet (discharge pressure).

heat: A form of energy.

humidity: Water vapor in the air (see relative humidity and absolute humidity).

I

insulator: A poor conductor of electricity or heat.

K

kinetic energy: Energy that is possessed by a moving body because of its motion; kinetic energy is in proportion to the body's mass (weight) and to the square of the velocity.

L

latent heat: Hidden heat required to change the state of a substance without changing the temperature. Latent heat cannot be felt or measured with a thermometer.

M

matter: Any substance that has weight and occupies space.

molecule: The smallest particle of a substance that can exist and still retain the properties of the substance.

P

potential energy: Energy that a body has because of its position; a weight raised to a height contains potential energy because it can do work coming down. Likewise, a tensed or compressed spring contains potential energy.

pressure: Force per unit area or force divided by area; usually measured in pounds-per-square-inch (psi).

R

radiation: The transfer of energy in waves.

refrigeration: Cooling an object or substance by removal of heat.

relative humidity: The amount of water vapor in the air compared to the amount the air could hold at a given temperature.

S

saturated vapor: A vapor that is in contact with the liquid it was generated from in a confined space, and is at the same temperature as the liquid. The water vapor in a tea kettle or pressure cooker is a saturated vapor.

sensible heat: Heat which can be felt or measured with a thermometer; sensible heat changes the temperature of a substance, but not the state.

specific heat: The quantity of heat in Btu's required to change the temperature of one pound of a substance one degree F.

sublimation: Conversion from the solid to the vapor state without passing through the liquid state.

suction pressure: Pressure at the compressor or inlet.

suction side: The low pressure inlet side of the compressor.

superheated vapor: A vapor that is not in contact with the generating liquid, and that has a higher temperature than the saturated vapor at the same pressure.

T

temperature: The measure of heat intensity or concentration in degrees; temperature is not a measure of heat quantity.

thermal: Of or pertaining to heat.

thermometer: A device which operates by thermal expansion and measures the intensity of heat (temperature).

V

vacuum: A condition of pressure less than atmospheric pressure. Vacuum can be measured in psi, but is more commonly measured in inches of mercury ("Hg). A perfect vacuum is 29.92 "Hg. This is based on the fact that a perfect vacuum above a column of mercury will support the column to a height of 29.92 inches.

vapor: A gas.

vaporization: The changing of a substance to the gaseous (vapor) state; vaporization is a general term, and includes evaporation, boiling and sublimation.

Appendices

The tables and charts in this *Appendix* as well as the definitions of terms in the *Glossary* will be useful to you as you continue your study of air conditioning and trouble shooting.

The fact that these types of references are readily available here should indicate the value of the publication as a textbook and as handy reference guide. Included in the *Appendix* are the following:

A. THI — Temperature - Humidity Index
B. Psychrometric Chart
C. Metric and English Conversion
D. Group I Refrigerants and Refrigerant Boiling Points
E. Temperature - Pressure Relationships for Freon, Conversion Charts and Formulas

Appendix A

Temperature-Humidity Index

Humidity and temperature in combination can cause us to feel uncomfortable. To express this degree of discomfort, the results of a series of tests were plotted on a chart and given the name of the *Temperature-Humidity Index (THI)**. The THI is a number which indicates that a certain percentage of people will feel uncomfortable due to a combination of temperature and humidity.

The *Index* is determined by adding the wet and dry bulb temperatures and multiplying by 0.4. Then a factor of 15 is added to the result. *As an example:* A wet bulb temperature of 65°F and a dry bulb temperature of 74°F will add up to 139°F. This sum, when multiplied by 0.4 will give a resultant of 55.6. Adding 15 to this gives a THI of 71. Under these conditions approximately 10% of the general population will feel discomfort due to this combination of temperature and humidity.

At a THI of 70..........10% of people
will be uncomfortable

At a THI of 75..........50% of people
will be uncomfortable

At a THI of 79........100% of people
will be uncomfortable

*This Index was developed by the U.S. Weather Bureau

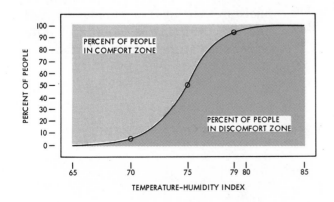

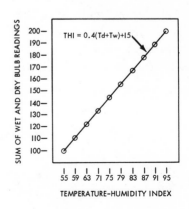

$$THI = 0.4(Td+Tw)+15$$

Appendix B

Psychrometric Chart

The most common way of representing the various properties of air and moisture is with a *psychrometric chart*. The psychrometric chart is simple to use in spite of its seeming complexity. Primarily it shows the relationship between the following factors:

1. Dry-bulb temperature
2. Wet-bulb temperature
3. Dew-point temperature
4. Percent humidity (relative humidity)
5. Moisture content
6. Pressure of water vapor (weight)

If two or more of these factors is known, the remaining factors can be found from the chart.

The dry-bulb lines on the chart are vertical; the wet-bulb lines slope down and to the right. Dew-point lines are the thin horizontal ones. The curved lines represent the percent of relative humidity.

Grains of moisture per pound of dry air are shown on the vertical axis on the left side of the chart.

To determine *dry-bulb temperature*, follow vertically down and read at the bottom of the scale. *Wet-bulb temperature* can be determined by following along the wet-bulb lines and reading at the intersection of the 100 percent relative humidity curve (saturation curve).

Relative humidity is read directly from the relative humidity curves. *Dew-point temperature* can be found by following horizontally to the intersection with the 100 percent relative humidity line.

Moisture content (absolute humidity) is determined by following horizontally to the scales on the right hand side of the chart. *Vapor pressure* for corresponding moisture content is determined by reading directly from the pressure of water vapor scale at the right of the chart.

See page 175 for Psychrometric Chart

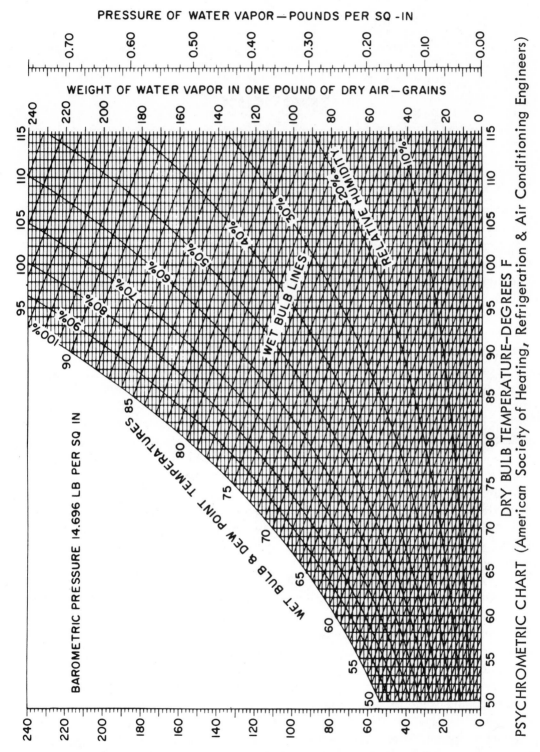

PRESSURE OF WATER VAPOR—POUNDS PER SQ -IN

WEIGHT OF WATER VAPOR IN ONE POUND OF DRY AIR—GRAINS

RELATIVE HUMIDITY

WET BULB LINES

WET BULB & DEW POINT TEMPERATURES

BAROMETRIC PRESSURE 14.696 LB PER SQ IN

DRY BULB TEMPERATURE—DEGREES F

PSYCHROMETRIC CHART (American Society of Heating, Refrigeration & Air Conditioning Engineers)

WEIGHT OF WATER VAPOR IN ONE POUND OF DRY AIR—GRAINS

Appendix C

Metric and English Conversions

Rapid expansion of trade and industry on an international basis in the past two decades has increased the need for understanding of both the *metric* or CGS (Centimeter-Gram-Second) system used by nearly all countries of the world and the *English* or FPS (Foot-Pound-Second) system used by the United States and some other English-speaking countries.

If the co-existence of two systems seems inconvenient, as it is, remember that in respect to worldwide agreement we are the exception. In view of the increasing need for a universal system to measure lengths, areas, volumes, weights, temperatures, etc., it now seems likely that the CGS system will ultimately replace the FPS system.

In 1972 a proposed bill to change from the use of the English system of units of measurement to the international metric system was introduced in the Congress of the United States. It proposed a voluntary ten year change-over period to accomplish the change. The Secretary of Commerce pointed to the need to meet export competition all over the world. Since the metric system has been legal in commerce and trade in this country for over a century (1866), the move is not without precedent. Other English system users started converting several years ago.

Table 1 lists factors for converting units from metric to English, while Table 2 lists factors for converting from English to metric units.

To convert a quantity from *metric* to *English* units:

1. Multiply by the factor shown in Table 1.
2. Use the resulting quantity "rounded off" to the number of decimal digits needed for practical application.
3. Wherever practical in semi-precision measurements, convert the decimal part of the number to the nearest common fraction.

To convert a quantity from *English* to *metric* units:

1. If the English measurement is expressed in fractional form, change this to an equivalent decimal form.
2. Multiply this quantity by the factor shown in Table 2.
3. Round off the result to the precision required.

Relatively small measurements, such as 17.3 cm, are generally expressed in equivalent millimeter form. In this example the measurement would be read as 173 mm.

TABLE 1 CONVERSION OF METRIC TO ENGLISH UNITS

LENGTHS:		WEIGHTS:	
1 MILLIMETER (mm)	= 0.03937 IN OR = 0.003281 FT	1 GRAM (g)	= 0.03527 OZ (AVDP)
1 CENTIMETER (cm)	= 0.3937 IN	1 KILOGRAM (kg)	= 2.205 LBS
1 METER (m)	= 3.281 FT OR 1.0937 YDS	1 METRIC TON	= 2205 LBS
1 KILOMETER (km)	= 0.6214 MILES	LIQUID MEASUREMENTS:	
AREAS:		1 CU CENTIMETER (cc)	= 0.06102 CU IN
1 SQ MILLIMETER	= 0.00155 SQ IN	1 LITER (= 1000 cc)	= 1.057 QUARTS OR 2.113 PINTS OR 61.02 CU IN
1 SQ CENTIMETER	= 0.155 SQ IN		
1 SQ METER	= 10.76 SQ FT OR 1.196 SQ YD	POWER MEASUREMENTS:	
		1 KILOWATT (kw)	= 1.341 HORSEPOWER
VOLUMES:		TEMPERATURE MEASUREMENTS:	
1 CU CENTIMETER	= 0.06102 CU IN	TO CONVERT DEGREES CENTIGRADE TO DEGREES FAHRENHEIT, USE THE FOLLOWING FORMULA: DEG F = (DEG C X 9/5) + 32	
1 CU METER	= 35.31 CU FT OR 1.308 CU YD		

SOME IMPORTANT FEATURES OF THE CGS SYSTEM ARE:
1 CC OF PURE WATER = 1 GRAM   PURE WATER FREEZES AT 0 DEGREES C AND BOILS AT 100 DEGREES C

TABLE 2 CONVERSION OF ENGLISH TO METRIC UNITS

LENGTHS:		WEIGHTS:	
1 INCH	= 2.540 CENTIMETERS OR 25.40 MILLIMETERS	1 OUNCE (AVDP)	= 28.35 GRAMS
1 FOOT	= 30.48 CENTIMETERS OR 304.8 MILLIMETERS	1 POUND	= 453.6 GRAMS OR 0.4536 KILOGRAM
1 YARD	= 91.44 CENTIMETERS OR 0.9144 METERS	1 (SHORT) TON	= 907.2 KILOGRAMS
		LIQUID MEASUREMENTS	
1 MILE	= 1.609 KILOMETERS	1 (FLUID) OUNCE	= 0.02957 LITER OR 28.35 GRAMS
AREAS:		1 PINT	= 473.2 CU CENTIMETERS
1 SQ IN	= 6.452 SQ CENTIMETERS OR 645.2 SQ MILLIMETERS	1 QUART	= 0.9463 LITER
1 SQ FT	= 929.0 SQ CENTIMETERS OR 0.0929 SQ METER	1 (U.S.) GALLON	= 3785 CU CENTIMETERS OR 3.785 LITERS
1 SQ YD	= 0.8361 SQ METER	POWER MEASUREMENTS	
VOLUMES:		1 HORSEPOWER	= 0.7457 KILOWATT
1 CU IN	= 16.39 CU CENTIMETERS	TEMPERATURE MEASUREMENTS	
1 CU FT	= 0.02832 CU METER	TO CONVERT DEGREES FAHRENHEIT TO DEGREES CENTIGRADE, USE THE FOLLOWING FORMULA: DEG C = 5/9 (DEG F –32)	
1 CU YD	= 0.7646 CU METER		

Appendix D

Group I Refrigerants and Refrigerant Boiling Points

GROUP 1 REFRIGERANTS

REFRIGERANT NUMBER	NAME
11	Trichloromonofluoromethane
12	Dichlorodifluoromethane
13	Monochlorotrifluoromethane
21	Dichloromonofluoromethane
22	Monochlorodifluoromethane
30	Methylene Chloride
113	Trichlorotrifluoroethane
114	Dichlorotetrafluoroethane
500	Dichlorodifluoromethane (73.8%) and Ethylidene Fluoride (26.2%)
502	Monochlorodifluoromethane (48.8%) and Monochloropentafluoroethane (51.2%)
744	Carbon Dioxide

178

REFRIGERANT BOILING POINTS

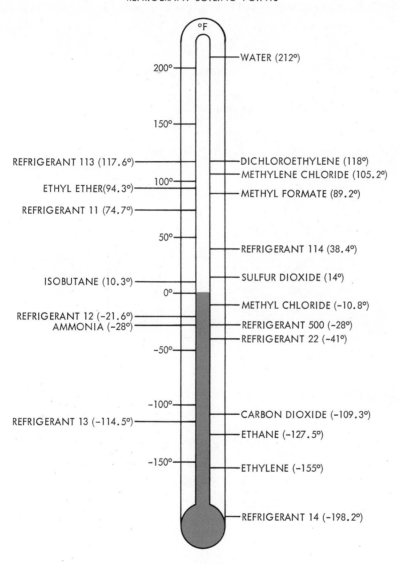

- WATER (212°)
- DICHLOROETHYLENE (118°)
- METHYLENE CHLORIDE (105.2°)
- REFRIGERANT 113 (117.6°)
- ETHYL ETHER(94.3°)
- METHYL FORMATE (89.2°)
- REFRIGERANT 11 (74.7°)
- REFRIGERANT 114 (38.4°)
- SULFUR DIOXIDE (14°)
- ISOBUTANE (10.3°)
- METHYL CHLORIDE (−10.8°)
- REFRIGERANT 12 (−21.6°)
- AMMONIA (−28°)
- REFRIGERANT 500 (−28°)
- REFRIGERANT 22 (−41°)
- CARBON DIOXIDE (−109.3°)
- REFRIGERANT 13 (−114.5°)
- ETHANE (−127.5°)
- ETHYLENE (−155°)
- REFRIGERANT 14 (−198.2°)

°F
200°
150°
100°
50°
0°
−50°
−100°
−150°

Appendix E

Temperature-Pressure Relationships for Freon, Conversion Chart and Formulas

TABLE I-2 TEMPERATURE-PRESSURE
RELATION

REFRIGERANT R-12 FREON	
FAHRENHEIT	PSI
-20	0.6
-15	2.4
-10	4.5
- 5	6.7
0	9.2
5	11.8
10	14.6
15	17.7
20	21.0
25	24.6
30	28.5
35	32.6
40	37.0
45	41.7
50	46.7
55	52.0
60	57.7
65	63.8
70	70.2
75	77.0
80	84.2
85	91.8
90	99.8
95	108.3
100	117.2
105	126.6
110	136.4
115	146.8
120	157.7
125	169.1
130	181.0
135	193.5
140	206.6
145	220.3
150	234.6

TEMPERATURE CONVERSION CHART

°F	°C	°F	°C	°F	°C	°F	°C	°F	°C
-15	-26.1	33	0.6	81	27.2	129	54.0	177	80.6
-14	-25.6	34	1.1	82	27.8	130	54.5	178	81.1
-13	-25.0	35	1.7	83	28.4	131	55.0	179	81.7
-12	-24.4	36	2.2	84	28.9	132	55.6	180	82.3
-11	-23.9	37	2.8	85	29.4	133	56.2	181	82.9
-10	-23.3	38	3.3	86	30.0	134	56.7	182	83.5
-9	-22.8	39	3.9	87	30.6	135	57.3	183	84.0
-8	-22.2	40	4.4	88	31.1	136	57.8	184	84.5
-7	-21.7	41	5.0	89	31.7	137	58.4	185	85.0
-6	-21.1	42	5.6	90	32.2	138	59.0	186	85.6
-5	-20.6	43	6.1	91	32.8	139	59.5	187	86.1
-4	-20.0	44	6.7	92	33.4	140	60.0	188	86.7
-3	-19.4	45	7.2	93	33.9	141	60.6	189	87.3
-2	-18.9	46	7.8	94	34.5	142	61.2	190	87.9
-1	-18.3	47	8.3	95	35.0	143	61.7	191	88.4
0	-17.7	48	8.9	96	35.6	144	62.3	192	89.0
1	-17.2	49	9.4	97	36.2	145	62.9	193	89.5
2	-16.7	50	10.0	98	36.7	146	63.4	194	90.0
3	-16.1	51	10.6	99	37.2	147	64.0	195	90.6
4	-15.6	52	11.1	100	37.8	148	64.5	196	91.1
5	-15.0	53	11.7	101	38.4	149	65.0	197	91.7
6	-14.4	54	12.2	102	38.9	150	65.6	198	92.3
7	-13.9	55	12.8	103	39.5	151	66.2	199	92.9
8	-13.3	56	13.3	104	40.0	152	66.7	200	93.4
9	-12.8	57	13.9	105	40.5	153	67.3	201	94.0
10	-12.2	58	14.4	106	41.1	154	67.8	202	94.5
11	-11.7	59	15.0	107	41.7	155	68.4	203	95.1
12	-11.1	60	15.6	108	42.3	156	69.0	204	95.6
13	-10.6	61	16.1	109	42.8	157	69.5	205	96.2
14	-10.0	62	16.7	110	43.4	158	70.0	206	96.8
15	-9.4	63	17.2	111	43.9	159	70.6	207	97.3
16	-8.9	64	17.8	112	44.5	160	71.2	208	97.9
17	-8.3	65	18.3	113	45.0	161	71.7	209	98.5
18	-7.8	66	18.9	114	45.6	162	72.3	210	99.0
19	-7.2	67	19.4	115	46.1	163	72.8	211	99.5
20	-6.7	68	20.0	116	46.7	164	73.4	212	100.0
21	-6.1	69	20.6	117	47.3	165	74.0	213	100.5
22	-5.6	70	21.1	118	47.8	166	74.5	214	101.1
23	-5.0	71	21.7	119	48.4	167	75.0	215	101.7
24	-4.4	72	22.2	120	49.0	168	75.6	216	102.2
25	-3.9	73	22.8	121	49.5	169	76.2	217	102.8
26	-3.3	74	23.4	122	50.0	170	76.7	218	103.4
27	-2.8	75	23.9	123	50.6	171	77.3	219	104.0
28	-2.2	76	24.4	124	51.2	172	77.9	220	104.5
29	-1.7	77	25.0	125	51.7	173	78.4	221	105.0
30	-1.1	78	25.6	126	52.3	174	79.0	222	105.6
31	-0.6	79	26.1	127	52.8	175	79.5	223	106.1
32	0	80	26.7	128	53.4	176	80.0	224	106.7

TEMPERATURE CONVERSION FORMULAS

1 To change Centigrade to Fahrenheit:

    a Multiply by 9/5
    b Then add 32°

2 To change Fahrenheit to Centigrade:

    a Subtract 32°
    b Multiply by 5/9

AN ALTERNATE IS:

$F = 1.8 \times C + 32°$

$C = F - 32° / 1.8$

Where:
F = Fahrenheit
C = Centigrade

Be certain the proper algebraic sign (positive or negative) is used

181

Index

Numerals in **bold type** refer to illustrations